L. Chesworth

A LESSON FOR EVERY DAY

MATHS

A & C Black • London

Published 2010 by A & C Black Publishers Limited
36 Soho Square, London W1D 3QY
www.acblack.com
ISBN 978-1-4081-2540-3
Copyright text © Hilary Koll, Steve Mills, Helen Glasspoole 2010
Editors: Dodi Beardshaw, Jane Klima, Marie Lister, Clare Robertson, Lynne Williamson
Compiled by Mary Nathan and Fakenham Photosetting

The authors and publishers would like to thank Ray Barker, Fleur Lawrence and Rifat Siddiqui for their advice in
producing this series of books.

A CIP catalogue record for this book is available from the British Library.

Printed and bound in Great Britain by Martins the Printers, Berwick-on-Tweed.

A & C Black uses paper produced with elemental chlorine-free pulp, harvested from managed sustainable forests.

Contents

Introduction

A Lesson for Every Day: Mathematics is a series of seven photocopiable activity books for the Foundation Stage and Key Stages 1 and 2, designed to be used during the daily maths lesson. The books focus on the skills and concepts outlined in the National Strategy's *Primary Framework for literacy and mathematics*. The activities are intended to be used in the time allocated to pupil activities; they aim to reinforce the knowledge and develop the facts, skills and understanding explored during the main part of the lesson and to provide practice and consolidation of the objectives contained in the Framework document.

A Lesson for Every Day: Mathematics Ages 10–11 supports the teaching of mathematics to children aged 10 to 11 by providing a series of activities to develop:

- processes for using and applying mathematics in real situations
- skills in talking about the mathematics in real situations
- essential skills in counting and recognising numbers
- the learning of simple number facts
- an understanding of ideas of addition, subtraction, multiplication and division
- spatial vocabulary in order to increase awareness of properties of shape and measurement concepts
- understanding of key concepts within the handling data cycle
- the skills of collecting, organising, presenting, analysing and interpreting data
- the language and key ideas of likelihood and chance linked to familiar events
- skills is finding the mode, mean, median and range of data.

On the whole, the activities are designed for children to work on independently, although due to the young age of the children, the teacher may need to read the instructions with the children to ensure that they understand the activity before they begin working on it.

Extension

Many of the activity sheets end with a challenge (**Now try this!**), which reinforces and extend children's learning, and provides the teacher with an opportunity for assessment. These might include harder questions, with numbers from a higher range, than those in the main part of the activity sheet. Some extension activities are open-ended questions and provide opportunity for children to think mathematically for themselves. Occasionally the extension activity will require additional paper or that the children write on the reverse of the sheet itself. Many of the activities encourage children to generate their own questions or puzzles for a partner to solve.

Organisation

Very little equipment is needed, but it will be useful to have available: coloured pencils, counters, cubes, scissors, dice, glue, coins, squared paper, number lines, grids and tracks, 2D and 3D shapes, a variety of different classroom items.

Where possible, children's work should be supported by ICT equipment, such as data handling programmes on interactive whiteboards, or computer software for moving pictures or photographs to show similarities and differences between groups and also charting information. It is also vital that children's experiences are introduced in real-life contexts, such as those portrayed in home/role play areas and through practical activities and number or nursery rhymes that they know. The teachers' notes at the foot of each page and the more detailed notes on pages 6 to 23 suggest ways in which this can be done effectively.

To help teachers select appropriate learning experiences for the children, the activities are grouped into sections within the book. However, the activities are not expected to be used in this order unless stated otherwise. The sheets are intended to support, rather than direct, the teacher's planning.

Some activities can be made easier or more challenging by masking or substituting numbers. You may wish to re-use pages by copying them onto card and laminating them.

Teachers' notes

Brief notes are provided at the foot of each page, giving ideas and suggestions for maximising the effectiveness of the activity sheets. These can be masked before copying.

Solutions can be found on pages 214 to 216.

Assessment

Use the completed activities as part of your day-to-day assessment to help you to build a picture of children's learning in order to plan future teaching and learning. Activities can also be used as examples of significant evidence for your periodic assessment. In order to help you to make reliable judgements about your pupils' attainment, the assessment focuses for each activity are given in the grids on pages 6–23.

Some of the activities provide opportunities for children to carry out self assessment. Encourage children to reflect on their learning and discuss with them whether there are areas that they feel they need to practise further.

The CD-ROM

All activity sheets can be found as PDF and Word versions on the accompanying CD-ROM. These can be printed or displayed on an interactive whiteboard. The Word versions can be customised in Microsoft Word in order to assist personalised learning.

They can be accessed through an interface that makes it easy to select worksheets and display them. You can also search for lessons that will meet a particular Assessment Focus for Assessing Pupils' Progress. For more information on system requirements, please see the inside front cover. If you have any questions regarding the *A Lesson For Every Day* CD-ROM, please email us at the address below. We will get back to you as soon as possible.
educationalsales@acblack.com

Whole class warm-up activities

The following activities provide some practical ideas that can be used to introduce or reinforce the main teaching part of the lesson, or provide an interesting basis for discussion.

Even, even, even

Write the number 18 on the board. Ask the children to suggest ways of adding three even numbers to make 18. After a while, introduce the idea that numbers can be repeated, for example 8 + 8 + 2. Write correct suggestions in a list and prompt the children to look for more. Ask: *How many twos have we written? How many eights? Are we missing any?* Encourage the children to suggest ways to organise the list in a systematic way to enable them to check for missed solutions.

Angle estimates

Join together two strips of card with a split pin to make an angle maker. Using the angle maker, hold up an acute angle and encourage the children to estimate its size. Make other acute or obtuse angles and ask the children to estimate each angle, using a large protractor to check their estimates. Award points for being within 5° or 10°.

Spiders

Draw a spider on the board with a decimal or fraction written on its body, for example 0.78 or $\frac{7}{12}$. Ask the children to suggest questions that give the decimal or fraction as the answer, and to write it on the spider's leg, for example 0.34 + 0.44, 1 − 0.22, 0.39 × 2.

Run-around fractions

Around the walls of the hall or classroom, pin pieces of paper showing a variety of fractions. Ask the children to stand in the middle of the room and call out a fraction that is equivalent to one around the room. Ask them to find this fraction and run to the correct sign. This can be played as a game where children who are standing by incorrect signs are out. Variations on this activity include calling out:
- a number and asking children to find a fraction with that denominator or numerator;
- a fraction question such as, 'Which fraction is half of one fifth?' or 'Which fraction is one quarter more than one half?'

Fraction and ratio features

Invite some children to the front of the class and pick a feature that some of them have, e.g. brown hair or wearing a skirt. Invite the rest of the class to say what fraction of the set of children have this feature e.g. 'three eighths of the children are wearing a tie' or 'four tenths of the children are girls'. Ask them then to describe the feature as a ratio, e.g. 'there are three children wearing a tie for every 5 children who are not' or 'the ratio of girls to boys is 4 to 6'. Where a ratio can be given as a simpler equivalent, such as 4 to 6 as 2 to 3, encourage the children in the set to get into identical groups to show this, e.g. two groups each with 2 girls to every 3 boys.

Follow the chain

Begin to write a series of numbers on the board where one digit changes each time, e.g. 3067, 3167, 3107, 4107, 4109, 4709. After each step ask the children to describe it, e.g. 'Add one hundred', 'Subtract sixty' etc. Invite children to continue the chain in the same way, until eventually the chain returns to its start number.

Quadrilateral crisis

Display a range of quadrilateral pictures on the board, such as parallelograms, rectangles, kites and trapeziums, labelled with letters. Begin to describe the properties of one of the shapes and ask children to identify which quadrilateral it is. Refer to the symmetries of the shape, its angles and even the properties of its diagonals.

Block A Counting, partitioning and calculating Unit 1

Activity name	Strand and learning objectives	Notes on the activities	Assessment Focus	Page number
Cheers!	**Using and applying mathematics** Explain reasoning and conclusions, using words, symbols or diagrams as appropriate	**Cheers!** *Processes: reason, explain, record, be systematic, generalise* Draw attention to the different ways of investigating this problem, such as using diagrams or tables to show the information. **Suggested questions:** • What do you think is the best way to show this information? • What patterns can you see? The solutions can be represented geometrically, like this: etc. The number of clinks can be recorded in a table to help the children to see the patterns. These patterns form a list of triangular numbers, where the number of clinks increases by 2, 3, 4, 5, 6, etc. each time.	Communicating	24
Mount Everest Fly me to the moon I am the champion	**Counting and understanding number** Find the difference between a positive and a negative integer, or two negative integers, in context	**Mount Everest** To emphasise that a difference is always given as a positive number, display a large number line and use a piece of string to show that the 'distance' between 3 and 5 is the same as between −3 and −5 and −2 and 0, and −1 and 1. **Suggested questions:** • How much do you think the temperature outside today has varied? • What do you think the temperature outside today might be? **Fly me to the moon** Explain that a difference is not negative, but rather always positive and that it just represents how far apart two numbers or temperatures are. **Suggested question:** • What is the temperature difference between these two temperatures? **I am the champion** To check the children's work, ask them to record their turns into a table, like this: | First number	Second number	Difference
---	---	---
−17	23	40 | The children could also check their answers using a number line or calculator. They could also draw their own grids and write their own positive and negative integers to create more games. **Suggested questions:** • Which is the smallest number in your opponent's grid? • How many more is −3 than −5?	Numbers and the number system	25 26 27
Snowflakes	**Counting and understanding number** Use decimal notation for tenths, hundredths and thousandths; partition, round and order decimals with up to three places, and position them on the number line	**Snowflakes** All the numbers in the snowflakes could be masked before copying and the children could make up their own snowflake sequences, counting on and back in tenths, hundredths or thousandths. **Suggested questions:** • Is this sequence increasing or decreasing? • How many tenths more is this number? • What is one thousandth more than 3·261?	Fractions, decimals, percentages, ratio and proportion	28
Totals and products	**Calculating** Calculate mentally with integers and decimals: U.t ± U.t; TU × U, TU ÷ U, U.t × U, U.t ÷ U	**Totals and products** Encourage the children to look for patterns in the answers and to predict the size of the answer of the next question, if written in order. **Suggested questions:** • How did you work this out? What strategies did you use? • Why isn't 64 × 10 a possible answer?	Mental methods	29

Block A Counting, partitioning and calculating Unit 2

Activity name	Strand and learning objectives	Notes on the activities	Assessment Focus	Page number
Prediction patterns	**Using and applying mathematics** Explain reasoning and conclusions, using words, symbols or diagrams as appropriate	**Prediction patterns** *Processes: predict, look for pattern* This activity can form the basis of some interesting sequencing work. When the children are making up their own sequences, remind them that they can have sequences where up to ten shapes are repeated. The children should be encouraged to explain their reasoning and to describe the patterns in the shapes and colours. **Suggested questions:** • How did you work that out? • What patterns did you notice? • How can you be sure? **Solutions:** 1 white triangle 2 grey square 3 white circle 4 grey triangle 5 white circle	Communicating	30

Activity name	Strand and learning objectives	Notes on the activities	Assessment Focus	Page number
Problems, problems	**Using and applying mathematics** Solve multi-step problems, and problems involving fractions, decimals and percentages; choose and use appropriate calculation strategies at each stage, including calculator use	**Problems, problems** *Processes: explain, reason, ask own questions* Discuss different units of measurement (such as mm, cm, m, km, g, kg, ml, l and also £ and p) and encourage the children to use different units for each word problem that they write. To get the children started, write some calculations on the board and together create appropriate word problems. Ensure the children understand that brackets mean that they should work out that part of the calculation first. The calculations can be altered to provide differentiation. SUGGESTED QUESTIONS: • What is your problem about? • What has to happen? Which part should you work out first? • How did you find this solution?	Problem solving	31
Pesky pets!		**Pesky pets!** *Processes: reason, look for pattern, compare, explain* At the start of the lesson, revise strategies for finding missing numbers in number sentences by writing an addition, subtraction, multiplication and division sum and masking the numbers in turn. Ask the children to say what calculation they would do to find each number, for example for $x \div 4 = 6$ they would multiply 4 by 6, whereas for $x + 4 = 6$ they would subtract 4 from 6. SUGGESTED QUESTION/PROMPT: • Which calculation did you put into the calculator to find this answer? Write it down.		32
Strategy sorting	**Calculating** Use a calculator to solve problems involving multi-step calculations	**Strategy sorting** *Processes: make decisions, explain, reason* Provide the children with calculators for this activity. At the end of the lesson, discuss the questions and see whether the children agree on the strategies to be used. SUGGESTED QUESTIONS: • Which method did you use? • Could you have done it another way? • Why did you decide to use a calculator here? • Could you have used a written method? How?	Solving numerical problems	33
Decimal puzzle: 1	**Counting and understanding number** Use decimal notation for tenths, hundredths and thousandths; partition, round and order decimals with up to three places, and position them on the number line	**Decimal puzzle: 1, and 2** These sheets are at three levels of difficulty. Children will require scissors and glue for this activity. Provide each child with a sheet and ask them to fit the small hexagons into the centres of the larger ones so that each decimal has been correctly rounded. If necessary, to make these activities a little simpler, ask the children to start with the larger hexagons and to round each decimal to the nearest whole number/tenth/hundredth. The answers can be written in the centre of the large hexagons. The children can then find the matching small hexagons showing the same numbers. SUGGESTED QUESTIONS: • How would you round this decimal to the nearest whole number/tenth/hundredth?	Fractions, decimals, percentages, ratio and proportion	34
Decimal puzzle: 2				35
Decimal hops	**Calculating** Calculate mentally with integers and decimals: U.t ± U.t, TU × U, TU ÷ U, U.t × U, U.t ÷ U	**Decimal hops** Remind children of the strategy of adding near multiples of 1 by adding the whole number and then adjusting the answer accordingly. Partitioning decimals could also be discussed as a suitable mental strategy. This is a much quicker and more effective strategy of adding these numbers than using a written method. SUGGESTED QUESTIONS: • How did you work this out? What strategies did you use? • How did you adjust the answer?	Mental methods	36
Annette's baguettes	**Calculating** Use efficient written methods to add and subtract integers and decimals, to multiply and divide integers and decimals by a one-digit integer, and to multiply two-digit and three-digit integers by a two-digit integer	**Annette's baguettes** Discuss suitable strategies for calculating the change, using written methods. Each amount could be subtracted from the money given, one at a time, or the total cost of the items found and then subtracting this from the amount of money given. SUGGESTED QUESTION/PROMPT: • How could you set it out in columns? • Show me what you would do.	Written methods	37
Digit discoveries		**Digit discoveries** At the start of the lesson, ask the children to explain how to use a written method to subtract decimals. Highlight 'rules' that mention aligning digits and decimal points, and what to do when the numbers in the calculation have different numbers of digits. SUGGESTED QUESTIONS: • What patterns do you notice? • Could the pattern continue? • What do you predict the answer will be?		38
Walter Wall carpets		**Walter Wall carpets** When answering the second part of the extension activity, the children should think about the cost of a 1 m length of carpet, for example £17 for the first carpet. The area of a 1 m length is 4 m² each time. Since 1 m² is 4 m² ÷ 4, the children then divide the cost of the 1 m length by 4 to find the area of 1 m², for example the area of 1 m² of the first carpet is £17 ÷ 4 = £4.25.		39
TU × TU: expanded		SUGGESTED QUESTIONS/PROMPT: • How could you work out this answer on paper? • How could you set it out in columns? **TU × TU: expanded and TU × TU: short** |	20	7
30	600	210	810 | 4	80	28	108 |			918 Once the children are able to use the grid above for multiplying, they will be ready to move on to these two template worksheets. The worksheets can be used to help children develop an understanding of the standard written method of multiplication of a pair of two-digit numbers, one in the expanded form and the other in the shorter contracted form. Suggested questions: • Why are there two zeros on the first line? (TU × TU: expanded) • Why is there one zero on the first line? (TU × TU: short)		40
TU × TU: short				41

Block A Counting, partitioning and calculating Unit 3

Activity name	Strand and learning objectives	Notes on the activities		Assessment Focus	Page number
Crazy creepy crawlies	**Using and applying mathematics** Explain reasoning and conclusions, using words, symbols or diagrams as appropriate	**Crazy creepy crawlies** *Processes: look for pattern, reason, be systematic, compare, check* Ensure that the children understand the problem fully before they begin the investigation. As they begin to work, encourage them to see that the different regions of the hoops count for different values in the total number, for example a creepy crawly in the central regions counts three times. **Suggested questions:** • How many solutions do you think there are? • Could we collect together all our solutions and check to see whether there are any others? • How could we arrange them to make sure?	**Sample solutions:**	Communicating	42
Calculator errors What do you notice?	**Using and applying mathematics** Solve multi-step problems, and problems involving fractions, decimals and percentages; choose and use appropriate calculation strategies at each stage, including calculator use **Calculating** Use a calculator to solve problems involving multi-step calculations	**Calculator errors** *Processes: explain, reason, ask own questions, record, check* This activity encourages the children to describe the strategies they would use to answer a calculation on a calculator, and to consider what error another person might have made. The calculations can be altered to provide differentiation. **Suggested questions:** • What do you think George might have done wrong? • What would you do? • What do you think the correct answer is? • Do you agree with Sam? Why/why not? **What do you notice?** *Processes: reason, compare, explain, look for pattern, trial and improvement, generalise* The children should work in pairs for this	activity so that they can discuss strategies. Invite them to explain to others how they solved the questions and ask them to make up their own puzzles to extend this investigation. It is important that they begin to notice that, despite the different contexts, the means of solving them is the same. All questions require the subtraction of three lots of a number from the total and then halving the answer. The questions could be altered to provide further practice. **Suggested questions:** • How did you find the answers? • Can you explain to the others what you noticed? • What is similar about these four questions? • Can you make up a fifth question that is also similar?	Problem solving Solving numerical problems	43 44
Weighty questions Coconut shy Decimal puzzle: 3	**Counting and understanding numbers** Use decimal notation for tenths, hundredths and thousandths; partition, round and order decimals with up to three places, and position them on the number line	**Weighty questions** Encourage children to compare the numbers by looking at the most significant digits first, in this case the units, then the tenths, hundredths and finally the thousandths. This should help them to remember the decreasing value of the digits. **Suggested questions:** How do you know that 3·099 is less than 3·55? Where would the number 3·264 belong in this list? How do you know? **Coconut shy** At the start of the lesson, practise counting in steps of 0·1, 0·01 and 0·001 from different start numbers. **Suggested question:** • Is this going up in steps of one tenth or one hundredth?	**Decimal puzzle: 3** These sheets are at three levels of difficulty. Children will require scissors and glue for this activity. Provide each child with a sheet and ask them to fit the small hexagons into the centres of the larger ones so that each decimal has been correctly rounded. If necessary, to make these activities a little simpler, ask the children to start with the larger hexagons and to round each decimal to the nearest whole number/tenth/hundredth. The answers can be written in the centre of the large hexagons. The children can then find the matching small hexagons showing the same numbers. **Suggested questions:** • How would you round this decimal to the nearest whole number/tenth/hundredth?	Fractions, decimals, percentages, ratio and proportion	45 46 47
Dice nets Going mental: 1 and 2	**Calculating** Calculate mentally with integers and decimals: U.t ± U.t, TU × U, TU ÷ U, U.t × U, U.t ÷ U	**Dice nets** Ask the children to make each dice for use with pages 49 and 50. The sheet can be photocopied onto A3 and stuck onto card. **Going mental: 1 and 2** The dice can be used for a variety of games and activities, such as those on the 'Going mental' sheets as number generators for a range of different calculations.	**Suggested questions:** • How would you work out 2·8 × 7? Would you use the same method or a different one to work out 9·5 × 7? Why? • Tell me an efficient method to work out 5·6 + 7·8. Would you use this method to work out 5·6 + 2·9? Why?	Mental methods	48 49–50
On the ball 9 to 1 challenge The mummy's riddle	**Calculating** Use efficient written methods to add and subtract integers and decimals, to multiply and divide integers and decimals by a one-digit integer, and to multiply two-digit and three-digit integers by a two-digit integer	**On the ball** If the children are using a column method, remind them to align the decimal points in each number so that digits of the same type are one below the other. **Suggested questions:** • Why did you choose to use that written method for this calculation? • What do you need to remember when using a column written method for subtraction? **'9 to 1 challenge** This activity provides practice in adding and subtracting numbers with different numbers of digits, including decimals and integers. You could change the wording 'some calculations' to a specified number for different attainment groups.	**The mummy's riddle** Ensure the children understand that the word 'integer' means a whole number. Remind them that their calculations must follow the rules set out in the riddle. **Suggested questions:** • Which questions did you try? • Did you find an answer larger than this?	Written methods	51 52 53

Block B Securing number facts, understanding shapes Unit 1

Activity name	Strand and learning objectives	Notes on the activities	Assessment Focus	Page number
Tile teaser	**Using and applying mathematics** Represent and interpret sequences, patterns and relationships involving numbers and shapes; suggest and test hypotheses; construct and use simple expressions and formulae in words then symbols (e.g. the cost of **C** pens at 15 pence each is 15**C** pence)	**Tile teaser** Processes: *test ideas, trial and improvement, look for pattern, generalise* This activity encourages the children to think about the nature of odd and even numbers and their sums. At the start of the lesson, ask the children to tell a partner everything they know about odd and even numbers. List these on the board. Highlight what they know about the sums and differences of odd and even numbers, for example: odd + even = odd. **SUGGESTED QUESTIONS:** • What patterns did you see? • How can you be sure that the total of this row will be even? • What is special about four numbers that have an even total? What are all the possibilities? **Sequence squares** Processes: *visualise, look for pattern, record, compare, reason, explain* To support children who find it difficult to write the next three numbers in each sequence, ask them to tell you the difference between adjacent patterns in the sequence. Show how this difference is added each time to give the next number in the sequence.	Reasoning	54
Sequence squares		As an extension, ask the children to write rules to tell others how to start and continue each of the sequences on the worksheet. **SUGGESTED QUESTIONS:** • What patterns did you notice in the sequences? • How can you say what comes next? • How could you describe this sequence? **Is it possible?** Processes: *look for pattern, reason, generalise, explain, justify* As an extension, ask the children to make up a similar puzzle for a partner to solve. **SUGGESTED QUESTIONS:** • Can you explain that? • Can you give me some examples? • Can you explain why this might be? • What do you know about the sum of the digits of multiples of 4/9/8/6? • How could you find out?		55
Is it possible?				56
Tables testing cards	**Number facts and calculations** Use knowledge of place value and multiplication facts to 10 × 10 to derive related multiplication and division facts involving decimals (e.g. 0.8 × 7, 4.8 ÷ 6)	**Tables testing cards** To give practice to children who need to reinforce their knowledge of times tables facts, you could change the numbers in the first column from decimals to single-digit whole numbers. **SUGGESTED QUESTIONS:** • Have you checked this answer? • How could you use the multiplication fact 3 × 6 = 18 to help you with this question?	Mental methods	57
Rounding riddles	**Number facts and calculations** Use approximations, inverse operations and tests of divisibility to estimate and check results	**Rounding riddles** As an alternative extension activity, the children could be asked to work out the approximate answers and then perform each calculation using an appropriate written method before checking their answers against the approximations. **SUGGESTED QUESTION:** • Can you tell me some pairs of factors of 240? **Hidden letters** At the start of the lesson, ask the children to say all the rules of divisibility they know. List these on the board. An alternative extension activity that is quite challenging, is to ask the children to draw a grid on squared paper, and to make up a puzzle where the numbers that are divisible by, say 9, can be coloured to form a letter. More confident children could even use numbers that are multiples of two numbers – say 3 and 5. Suggested question: • What multiples are common to 3 and 5? **Inverses in verse** Before the children start the activity, ask them to say what the inverse operation would be for different calculations. Ask them to explain why using inverses is a good way to check answers. **SUGGESTED QUESTION:** • What is the inverse operation you would use to check this multiplication/division?	Mental methods	58
Hidden letters			Operations and relationships between them	59
Inverses in verses				60
Cuboid crazy: 1 and 2	**Understanding shape** Describe, identify and visualise parallel and perpendicular edges or faces; use these properties to classify 2-D shapes and 3-D solids	**Cuboid crazy: 1 and 2** Before giving the children either worksheet, discuss how letters can be used to describe the edges and faces of 3-D shapes, for example using the letters at the vertices of a face to describe it, or using the letters of the two end-points of an edge to describe it. Explain how the letters are usually given in alphabetical order, and run clockwise around a shape. **SUGGESTED QUESTION:** • Can you colour the face ABCD, or the edge AB? **Path of truth** This activity need not be played as a game. The children could work individually or in pairs to decide whether each statement is true or false and record the answers. **SUGGESTED QUESTIONS:** • How many edges meet at vertex B? • Are all the edges that meet at B perpendicular to each other?	Properties of shape	61–62
Path of truth				63
Cut it out!	**Understanding shape** Make and draw shapes with increasing accuracy and apply knowledge of their properties	**Cut it out!** Provide the children with squared paper so that they can test their ideas and create their own puzzles as an extension activity. **SUGGESTED QUESTIONS:** • Before you cut these out, explain to me why you think you will have to cut the shape here. • Why would cutting the shape here not work?	Properties of shape	64

Block B Securing number facts, understanding shapes Unit 2

Activity name	Strand and learning objectives	Notes on the activities	Assessment Focus	Page number
House building	**Using and applying mathematics** Tabulate systematically the information in a problem or puzzle; identify and record the steps or calculations needed to solve it, using symbols where appropriate; interpret solutions in the original context and check their accuracy	**House building** *Processes: explain, reason, compare, visualise* Let the children organise the information in their own way before rewriting the revised 'jobs to do' list, but draw attention to good strategies involving a systematic approach. Encourage the children to look at the clues in any order they choose. **SUGGESTED QUESTIONS:** • How did you organise the information? • What did you write down? • What did this clue tell you?	Communicating	65
Logical thinking		**Logical thinking** *Processes: visualise, compare, reason* Explain to the children that when something is 'next to' another it can be horizontally or vertically next to it, but not diagonally. As a hint for question 2, tell the children that there are three red shapes. **SUGGESTED QUESTIONS:** • How easy did you find this? • Did you work through the clues in order? • Would it have helped if you had worked through in a different order?	Problem solving	66
Equation persuasion	**Using and applying mathematics** Represent and interpret sequences, patterns and relationships involving numbers and shapes; suggest and test hypotheses; construct and use simple expressions and formulae in words then symbols (e.g. the cost of C pens at 15 pence each is $15C$ pence)	**Equation persuasion** *Processes: reason, look for pattern, explain, visualise, compare, trial and improvement* The numbers in the shapes could be changed to provide more variety, although the new numbers should be selected carefully to match some or all of the equations. **SUGGESTED QUESTIONS:** • Do you think these equations would be true for other numbers? • How could you find out? • Why do you think this is?	Reasoning	67
Animal magic				68
Grid riddles		**Grid riddles** *Processes: reason, test ideas, explain, look for pattern* Questions 7, 8 and 9 require the children to write the equations that match the grids of numbers. Encourage the children to write their ideas for each equation and to test each set of numbers against it to check that they are correct. **SUGGESTED QUESTIONS:** • What patterns did you notice? • How could you express this using the letters A and B? **Animal magic** *Processes: reason, test ideas, explain, trial and improvement, look for pattern* Draw attention to the strategies that the children use to solve these problems, such as using trial and improvement strategies, drawing each situation, using tables or other approaches.		69
Robot squares	**Number facts and calculations** Use knowledge of multiplication facts to derive quickly squares of numbers to 12 × 12 and the corresponding squares of multiples of 10	**Robot squares** The cards could be copied onto A3 and/or laminated for a more permanent resource. Ensure the children are familiar with the notation of raising a 2 to represent a number squared. Demonstrate that when a number is squared it is multiplied by itself and show a square array as an example.	Mental methods	70
Division testing cards	**Number facts and calculations** Use knowledge of place value and multiplication facts to 10 × 10 to derive related multiplication and division facts involving decimals (e.g. 0.8 × 7, 4.8 ÷ 6)	**Division testing cards** These testing activities can be photocopied onto thin card and laminated to provide more permanent classroom resources. If the worksheet is laminated, the children could write answers on scraps of paper or on the sheets themselves in temporary marker pen. Encourage the children to The games and activities suggested in the Teachers' note on the page can be played individually or in pairs. **SUGGESTED QUESTIONS:** • What does the raised little 2 mean in 11²? • What does 'seven squared' mean? How could you write that as a calculation? mark their own so that they have an opportunity to see which facts they have made errors with. **SUGGESTED QUESTIONS:** • Have you checked this answer? • How could you use the multiplication fact 3 × 0.6 = 1.8 to work out 1.8 ÷ 3?	Mental methods Mental methods	71
Conveyor belts	**Number facts and calculations** Recognise that prime numbers have only two factors and identify prime numbers less than 100; find the prime factors of two-digit numbers	**Conveyor belts** This diagram should only be used to find which numbers are prime up to 100, as for larger numbers it is necessary to check whether they are multiples of other larger primes, such as 11, 13, 17, 19 etc. Ensure the children understand that they should complete all eight lines in each section. Before copying the activity sheet for more confident children, mask the second bullet point so that they work mentally. Less confident children could identify prime numbers less than 50. **SUGGESTED QUESTIONS:** • How did you check whether the number was a multiple of 5? • Why do you think it is not necessary to check whether the number is a multiple of 4, 6, 8 etc?	Mental methods	72 73
Prime suspect				
Sponsored sports	**Calculating** Use a calculator to solve problems involving multi-step calculations	**Sponsored sports** The children might like to plan a sponsored sports event of their own. **SUGGESTED QUESTIONS:** • How did you answer this question? • What did you key into the calculator?	Solving numerical problems	74
Shape sort: 1 and 2	**Understanding shape** Describe, identify and visualise parallel and perpendicular edges or faces; use these properties to classify 2-D shapes and 3-D solids	**Shape sort: 1 and 2** Encourage the children to notice where a criterion is negative, for example 'has no right angles', as this can sometimes cause confusion when sorting shapes. Shape sort: 1 can be used independently for a shape game. The children work in pairs and one player secretly chooses one of the shapes. The children must guess which shape it is by asking questions to which the first player can only answer 'yes' or 'no'. This activity is very useful in encouraging and developing questioning skills. **SUGGESTED QUESTIONS:** • How do you know that that shape has at least one line of symmetry?	Properties of shape	75–76
3-D detective		• Tell me the name of another shape that has all equal sides but no right angles. • What is the same about a square and rhombus? What is different? • What is the same about shapes 5 and 7? What is different? • Draw a triangle that is different to 5 and 7. How is your triangle different? **3-D detective** As a further extension, the children could name each of the shapes shown on the worksheet and list all of their properties. **SUGGESTED QUESTIONS:** • What shapes are the faces of a cube/cuboid/triangular prism? • Are its faces/edges parallel or perpendicular?		77

Activity name	Strand and learning objectives	Notes on the activities	Assessment Focus	Page number
Tetrahedra	**Understanding shape** Make and draw shapes with increasing accuracy and apply knowledge of their properties	**Tetrahedra** A second activity can be completed using the same worksheet, where the children draw and make tetrahedra exactly half the size of the one shown. Similarly, these are stuck to each face of the larger tetrahedron (so that the corners of the smaller tetrahedra touch the mid-points of the edges of the larger one) to make a shape with eight vertices and 24 triangular faces. **SUGGESTED QUESTIONS:** • Look at the net. How many faces has it? • What shape are the faces? • Are the faces regular?	Properties of shape	78

Block B Securing number facts, understanding shapes Unit 3

Activity name	Strand and learning objectives	Notes on the activities	Assessment Focus	Page number
Table challenges	**Using and applying mathematics** Tabulate systematically the information in a problem or puzzle; identify and record the steps or calculations needed to solve it, using symbols where appropriate; interpret solutions in the original context and check their accuracy	**Table challenges** *Processes: visualise, reason, be systematic, look for pattern, check* The children could use several methods to tackle each of the problems, for example for Challenge 1: 2 × one tea and three cakes (statement 1) = two teas and six cakes = 2 × £3 = £6 two teas and six cakes – two teas and two cakes (statement 2) = four cakes = £6 – £3.60 = £2.40 four cakes ÷ 4 = one cake = £2.40 ÷ 4 = £0.60 Since one tea and three cakes costs £3, then one tea = £3 – (3 × £0.60) = £1.20 They can use this information to fill in the rest of the table. **SUGGESTED QUESTIONS/PROMPT:** • What patterns do you notice in the numbers in the table? • How did you work this out? • Explain what the table shows us.	Communicating, Problem solving	79
Square numbers, A general rule, Formula fun	**Using and applying mathematics** Represent and interpret sequences, patterns and relationships involving numbers and shapes; suggest and test hypotheses; construct and use simple expressions and formulae in words then symbols (e.g. the cost of C pens at 15 pence each is $15C$ pence)	**Square numbers** *Processes: reason, test ideas, explain, visualise, generalise, justify, check* Write the following square numbers on the board for the children to refer to: 1, 4, 9, 16, 25, 36, 49, 64, 81, 100, 121, 144, 169, 196, 225, 256, 289, 324, 361, 400... Encourage the children to give their own explanations for why they think the statements are true. You could discuss the following explanations with higher attaining children: **1** Any even number can be written as $2n$ (where n is a whole number 1, 2, 3...). Any odd number can be written as $2n + 1$. Squaring $(2n + 1)$ gives $(2n + 1) × (2n + 1) = 4n^2 + 4n + 1$. So the square of any odd number can be written as $4n^2 + 4n + 1$, for some natural number n. $4n^2 + 4n + 1$ can be written as $4(n^2 + n) + 1$. Since n is a whole number, n^2 is also a whole number and so is $(n^2 + n)$. Therefore, $4(n^2 + n)$ is a multiple of 4 and so $4n^2 + 4n + 1$ must be 1 more than a multiple of 4. **2** Consecutive square numbers follow the pattern odd, even, odd, even, etc. The total of an odd and an even number is always odd so the sum of two consecutive square numbers will always be odd. **3** If our consecutive numbers are n and n + 1, when we square them we get n^2 and $(n + 1)^2 = n^2 + 2n + 1$. Their difference $= (n^2 + 2n + 1) – n^2 = 2n + 1 = n + (n + 1)$. So this is the sum of our two consecutive numbers. **4** If we call the multiple of 3, 3n, then $(3n)^2 = 9n^2$. Therefore, the square number must be a multiple of 9. **5** 5^2 is 25, and 2 + 5 = 7 which is odd. However, $11^2 = 121$, and 1 + 2 + 1 = 4 which is even. **6** If we call the consecutive odd numbers, n + 1 and n + 3 (n being even), and multiply them (n + 1)(n + 3), we get $n^2 + 4n + 4$. This can be written as $(n + 2) × (n + 2)$ or $(n + 2)^2$ which tells us that this is an even number squared. (In fact, it is the even number that lies between the two odd numbers.) **SUGGESTED QUESTIONS:** • How can you be sure that this is true? • Can you give me some examples? • Can you explain why this might be? • What do you know about odd and even numbers? **A general rule** *Processes: explain, reason, generalise* As a further extension, the children could make up formulae for other situations, for example the number of children having school dinners every day or the cost of cinema tickets. **SUGGESTED QUESTIONS:** • How does an expression or formula help you? • How can we use the formula to find the number of weeks in seven years? **Formula fun** *Processes: explain, reason, record, generalise* At the start of the lesson, discuss how the children know what operation to use to solve a word problem. Ask them to pose word problems that involve addition, subtraction, multiplication and division. Take one of their problems and replace one of the numbers or amounts by a letter. Ask the children to say how their answer would change and what it would be. Ask the children to show you how they could write their answer. **SUGGESTED QUESTION:** • How does an expression or formula help you?	Reasoning	80, 81, 82
Square secrets	**Number facts and calculations** Use knowledge of multiplication facts to derive quickly squares of numbers to 12 × 12 and the corresponding squares of multiples of 10	**Square secrets** Demonstrate how a calculation such as 60 × 60 can be written as 6 × 10 × 6 × 10 and as 6 × 6 × 100. Encourage the children to square multiples of 10 in this way, before tackling this activity. **SUGGESTED QUESTION:** • Can you write some more questions like these to make the French word for square (carré)?	Mental methods	83
Magic squares	**Number facts and calculations** Use knowledge of place value and multiplication facts to 10 × 10 to derive related multiplication and division facts involving decimals (e.g. 0.8 × 7, 4.8 ÷ 6)	**Magic squares** This activity provides practice in multiplying whole numbers by tenths and then adding sets of three decimals together. **SUGGESTED QUESTION:** • Which known facts did you use to help you?	Mental methods	84

Activity name	Strand and learning objectives	Notes on the activities	Assessment Focus	Page number
Prime factor compactor American football Primes, squares and multiples	**Number facts and calculations** Recognise that prime numbers have only two factors and identify prime numbers less than 100; find the prime factors of two-digit numbers	**Prime factor compactor** A prime factor is a factor that is prime. All numbers can be written as a product of prime factors, unless the number itself is prime. SUGGESTED QUESTION: • Prime numbers are sometimes called the building blocks of numbers. Why do you think this is? **American football** Alternative numbers could be written on this sheet before copying to provide wider variety or more challenge. SUGGESTED QUESTION: • Have you checked your answers? **Primes, squares and multiples** This activity requires the children to use what they know about prime numbers, square numbers and multiples of 10. At the start of the lesson, ask the children to tell you facts about the different types of number, for example multiples of 10 have last digit zero, the only even prime number is 2, 1 is not a prime number. SUGGESTED QUESTIONS: • How did you work out that 16 and 81 are the two prime numbers that total 97? • Why couldn't you use 40 and 2 as the two numbers to total 42?	Mental methods	85 86 87
Just for pets	**Calculating** Use a calculator to solve problems involving multi-step calculations	**Just for pets** In this activity, the children work out which of a set of items is the best value. Begin by discussing what the activity means, by using the example of packs of crisps: is buying eight separate packs of crisps cheaper or more expensive than buying a pack of eight packets? SUGGESTED QUESTIONS: • Why did you choose that method for this question? • What did you key into the calculator to show £0.78?	Solving numerical problems	88
Cutting corners	**Understanding shape** Describe, identify and visualise parallel and perpendicular edges or faces; use these properties to classify 2-D shapes and 3-D solids	**Cutting corners** Children sometimes lack experience of examining the properties of 3-D shapes. Skeletal shapes can help them to see the number of edges that join at each vertex and the number and shapes of the faces. SUGGESTED QUESTIONS: • Do you know the name of this shape? • What makes a prism different from a pyramid?	Properties of shape	89
Compass mastery Dodecahedra	**Understanding shape** Make and draw shapes with increasing accuracy and apply knowledge of their properties	**Compass mastery** This worksheet can be given to the children in pairs. After reading the instructions carefully, the children should try to draw the shape, becoming skilled enough in each attempt to be able to teach others how to draw the shape afterwards. Check that the children know that 'arc' refers to part of the circumference of a circle. SUGGESTED QUESTIONS: • What do you have to do in order to use a pair of compasses to draw a circle of radius 6 cm? • I want to draw a circle with the same centre as that one, but with a radius of 10 cm. What should I do? **Dodecahedra** Ensure that each child has a regular pentagon to draw around as a template for the extension activity. The children can then make their own templates from cardboard. SUGGESTED QUESTIONS: • Look at the net. How many faces has it? • What shape are the faces? • Are the faces regular?	Properties of shape	90 91

Block C Handling data and measures Unit 1

Activity name	Strand and learning objectives	Notes on the activities	Assessment Focus	Page number
Let's enquire: 1 and 2 Birthday survey: 1 and 2	**Using and applying mathematics** Suggest, plan and develop lines of enquiry: collect, organise and represent information, interpret results and review methods; identify and answer related questions	**Let's enquire: 1 and 2** Processes: make decisions, plan, record, co-operate, predict These worksheets encourage the children to make decisions and to plan how to follow lines of enquiry by collecting data. SUGGESTED QUESTIONS: • How did you decide what to do? • What do you think the outcome might be? **Birthday survey: 1 and 2** Processes: make decisions, plan, record, co-operate, predict, test ideas, explain There are different ways of collecting the data for the survey on page 41. Some children might choose to tally the months of the year in a table and then write a list of numbers to show the dates, whereas others might just compile a list of birthdays. Others might draw a table for the seasons or expect those questioned to give the day of the week of their birthday, whereas others might use a calendar and find out themselves.	Reasoning	92–93 94–95
Finding out	**Handling data** Solve problems by collecting, selecting, processing, presenting and interpreting data, using ICT where appropriate; draw conclusions and identify further questions to ask	**Finding out** This activity focuses on how to plan an investigation. Through paired discussions, the children should be encouraged to think about how data could be collected and how this could be done accurately. Concepts of average amounts and typical lengths of time can be linked to the mean average. The question relating to school population is more straightforward and could be attempted by less confident children first. Questions linked to topic work or local issues or environment could be substituted using the CD-ROM resource. SUGGESTED QUESTIONS: • How could you collect this data? • How accurate do you think the data would be?	Processing and representing data Interpreting data	96

Activity name	Strand and learning objectives	Notes on the activities	Assessment Focus	Page number
Testing times You are what you eat	**Handling data** Construct and interpret frequency tables, bar charts with grouped discrete data, and line graphs; interpret pie charts	**Testing times** This activity shows grouped data of children's test scores. Discuss how the data has been organised, and check that children understand that each bar shows how many children have scored marks in that group; it is not possible to say from the graph how many children scored, for example, nine marks. Explain that grouped bar charts are used when there would otherwise be very many categories. The extension activity prompts the children to notice the normal distribution of data, although terminology is not required at this stage. **Suggested questions:** • Why do you think the data is grouped like this? • What do you notice about the groupings? **You are what you eat** This activity introduces the children to pie charts. Warm-up activities could include a focus on division, factors and fractions. Discuss the first pie chart and explain that each mark on the circumference of the circle shows 10°. In this pie chart, the total weight of the ingredients was 360 g, so 10° stands for 10 g. This means that the children can use the chart to give the weight of the different ingredients. Use the second pie chart to show that pie charts can represent different totals. Ask the children to say what fraction of the whole each mark on the circle represents (), and ask them to work out one-twelfth of 24. As an extension, the children could list the similarities and differences between the two pie charts. **Suggested questions:** • Which weighed more, the sugar or the eggs? How do you know? • How do you know how many children had crisps?	Processing and representing data	97 98
Home on the range: 1 and 2 Different modes: 1 and 2 Paul's pool party In the middle: 1 and 2	**Handling data** Describe and interpret results and solutions to problems using the mode, range, median and mean	**Home on the range: 1 and 2** At the start of the lesson, write two sets of numbers on the board, for example 21, 28, 29, 30, 32, 35 and 11, 45, 63, 72, 81, 112. Ask the children to describe the sets of numbers. Introduce the range as a way to describe whether the pieces of data in a set are close in size or far apart. In the first set of numbers, the range (the difference between the highest and the lowest value) is 14; in the second set the range is 101. **Suggested questions:** • What does the 'range' mean? • How could you calculate this? **Different modes: 1 and 2** Discuss the concept of the mode and how the mode could be a value, group of data, colour, etc. The activity shows different representations of data so that the children can see how the mode applies to different scenarios. As a class look at real-life examples, such as ordering stock for a shoe shop to show why different numbers of different-sized shoes are ordered. **Suggested questions:** • What does the 'mode' mean? • What is the mode of this set of data (for example colour of eyes, number of siblings)? **Paul's pool party** The sets of data provided are all linked to a swimming pool and require the children to calculate the mean. The data has been planned so that the children should not need a calculator. Encourage the children to think about whether their answer is reasonable. Talk about the mean as the most commonly used 'average'. The last set of data shows how such an average can be meaningless, especially given that a splash pool is not very big! As an extension, ask the children to give the missing value for this set of data with a mean of 8: 6, 13, 9, 3, (9). **Suggested questions:** • What is the 'mean' average? • Is the mean always a number in the set of data? How do you know? **In the middle: 1 and 2** Talk about how the median can be useful if there are extreme values that would otherwise skew the mean average. Ensure that the children understand why the data needs to be ordered first. **Suggested questions:** • What does the 'median' mean? • What happens if there is an even number of pieces of data?	Interpreting data	99–100 101–102 103 104–105

Block C Handling data and measures Unit 2

Activity name	Strand and learning objectives	Notes on the activities	Assessment Focus	Page number
Weather station	**Handling data** Solve problems by collecting, selecting, processing, presenting and interpreting data, using ICT where appropriate; draw conclusions and identify further questions to ask	**Weather station** Building on previous/current work on the topic of 'weather', the children think about data that could be collected over a month/half a term. Examples might include: presence/absence of sun, rain, hail, snow; different types of cloud; amount of rain collected per day/week; force of wind; direction of wind (linked to compass work). The children plan and develop lines of enquiry to then collect, organise and represent information relating to their chosen area. Organise groups so that a range of data is collected. The children could then interpret results and review methods of data collection, suggesting improvements for another time. In groups, the children can identify related questions about their data for others in the class to answer. **Suggested questions:** • Is that a fair way to collect rainfall? • How could you record the data to ensure it is accurate?	Processing and representing data Interpreting data	106
Salad bar Stretchy statistics: 1 and 2 Plant scale: 1 and 2	**Handling data** Construct and interpret frequency tables, bar charts with grouped discrete data, and line graphs; interpret pie charts	**Salad bar** This activity reinforces the children's understanding of the use of a tally to collect data over time. The focus is on the total number of portions served for each salad type. As an extension, the children could organise the data for each day of the week to consider whether salad was a more popular choice on any particular day. Different aspects of this data could be represented on blank bar charts. It could also be used (with teacher support) to show proportions of totals using pie charts. **Suggested questions:** • How many portions of mixed pepper were served on Thursday? • Which was the least popular salad choice? **Stretchy statistics: 1 and 2** The focus of this activity is on the nature of the data and that a line graph is appropriate because the interim points are meaningful. This could be demonstrated by adding smaller weights to a spring and recording the amount the spring stretches. The children could carry out the practical investigation described, before or after completing the worksheets. Their own data from testing elastic bands/springs could be used instead and plotted on different graphs. The elasticity of the bands/spring will determine the size of weights that should be added. **Suggested questions:** • How much did the spring stretch when 600 g were added? • How can you work out how long the spring would be if 450 g were added? **Plant scale: 1 and 2** This activity requires the children to understand the concept of finding a proportion of a given amount. Each question asks the children to demonstrate a different aspect of their understanding – finding given numbers of plants and finding the total of all plants represented. **Suggested questions:** • In which week were the most orchids sold? • How can you calculate the total number of plants sold?	Processing and representing data	107 108–109 110–111

Activity name	Strand and learning objectives	Notes on the activities	Assessment Focus	Page number
Side orders Best average Cube collection	**Handling data** Describe and interpret results and solutions to problems using the mode, range, median and mean	**Side orders** Discuss the data given and how the format of the table clearly shows the orders of one side dish across the week and of different dishes for each day. The children may need a calculator to work out the mean averages as decimals are involved. **SUGGESTED QUESTIONS:** • How many orders of chips were there across the week? • What is the range for the orders of mixed peppers? **Best average** By calculating the mean, median and mode for different sets of data, the children are asked to consider which average they think is best for the context given. Discuss how one average could be chosen intentionally to mislead.	Interpreting data	112 113 114
		SUGGESTED QUESTIONS: • Which average do you think is the most representative for that data? • Why would you choose that average? **Cube collection** Talk about why giving everyone three attempts and then finding the average score is often used to reduce effects of first attempts and practice. The children will have to justify their choice of average, given that everyone is going to want to use the one that shows their score as the best. **SUGGESTED QUESTIONS:** • How will you measure how many cubes are picked up? • Why do you think that average is the fairest one to use?		
Chess guess: 1 and 2 Chance landing	**Handling data** Describe and predict outcomes from data using the language of chance or likelihood	**Chess guess: 1 and 2** No knowledge of chess is needed for this activity, although it would be useful to have a chess set available so that all children are familiar with the number and name of each piece. Based on the number and colour of pieces, the children work out the probability of different pieces being chosen at random. Play a game of guessing or bingo with chess pieces first, so that children can get used to the chess pieces. **SUGGESTED QUESTIONS:** • Why do you think that picking a rook is more likely than picking a king? • Which pieces are equally likely to be picked from the chess set? **Chance landing** This activity uses spinners as a resource to generate data about chance. Blank spinners can be used to reinforce and extend these concepts. The spinners are best copied onto card. Ensure that the children cut along the edges carefully so as not to affect which side the spinner lands on. Supervision might be needed when making the hole through the centre of the spinner. **SUGGESTED QUESTIONS:** • Why do you think that spinner is more likely to land on the shaded part? • Can you shade the spinner so that it is twice as likely to land on blue than on red?	Interpreting data	115–116 117
Can you do better?	**Measuring** Select and use standard metric units of measure and convert between units using decimals to two places (e.g. change 2.75 litres to 2750 ml, or vice versa)	**Can you do better?** At the start of the lesson, remind the children that 1000 ml is the same as 1 litre and pass round a container, bottle or carton that holds a litre of liquid. This will help the children to develop a sense of how much 1 litre or 1000ml is. Remind the children that 100 cm is the same as 1 metre and discuss how far this distance is in relation to a metre stick. Similarly, discuss other units of length. Remind the children that 1000g is the same as 1 kilogram and pass round weights so that they can develop a sense of how heavy 1 kilogram or 1000g is. **SUGGESTED PROMPT/QUESTIONS:** • Explain how you know that 0.157 kg is equal to 157 g. • Is 350cm longer or shorter than 3500mm? How do you know?	Measures	118
In the science lab	**Measuring** Read and interpret scales on a range of measuring instruments, recognising that the measurement made is approximate and recording results to a required degree of accuracy; compare readings on different scales, for example when using different instruments	**In the science lab** At the start of the lesson, draw a variety of number lines with 10 intervals on the board and mark the ends in different ways, for example 0 and 20, 100 and 250, 500 and 1000. Ask the children to say what each interval is worth on each line, and how they know. Draw an arrow on each line and invite the children to say the value that is indicated. **SUGGESTED QUESTION/PROMPT:** • How do you know what each interval is worth on this scale? • Draw an arrow on this scale to show 0.85 kg.	Measures	119

Block C Handling data and measures Unit 3

Activity name	Strand and learning objectives	Notes on the activities	Assessment Focus	Page number
In conclusion: 1, 2, 3, and 4	**Handling data** Solve problems by collecting, selecting, processing, presenting and interpreting data, using ICT where appropriate; draw conclusions and identify further questions to ask	**In conclusion: 1, 2, 3 and 4** The children should work in pairs on these four activities. The focus of this activity is for the children to consider what the data does and does not tell the reader and, therefore, what conclusions can and cannot be drawn. The activity can also be used to encourage children to think about further lines of enquiry based on each set of data. The role of experience and preconceived ideas is also considered through statements such as 'Girls are better at football than boys', which may shape the way that the reader interprets the data. **SUGGESTED QUESTIONS:** • Why do you agree/disagree with that statement? • Is it fair to draw that conclusion from this data?	Processing and representing data Interpreting data	120–123

Activity name	Strand and learning objectives	Notes on the activities	Assessment Focus	Page number
Miles to kilometres Per 100 grams	**Handing data** Construct and interpret frequency tables, bar charts with grouped discrete data, and line graphs; interpret pie charts	**Miles to kilometres** Using other graphs, such as British pounds to Euros, model how to read off the correct values. Such graphs can be compared to ready reckoners, which some children may find easier to interpret but which do not give interim amounts. **SUGGESTED QUESTIONS:** • How many whole kilometres are there in 5 miles? • What is the equivalent measurement for 70 kilometres? **Per 100 grams** The data taken from a leading brand could be compared with other cereal bars to consider proportions of different nutrients. Although a bar might advertise that it is low in fat, it might be very high in sugar. The children should have access to calculators as they work out percentages for different weight bars. **SUGGESTED QUESTIONS:** • How many grams of fat are there in a bar that weighs 120 g? • How can you work this out?	Processing and representing data	124 125
Cheeky Chalky Beijing 2008	**Handling data** Describe and interpret results and solutions to problems using the mode, range, median and mean	**Cheeky Chalky** Although the concepts of range and average are not new, the children are now required to find the missing value using the given average. As a whole class, talk about what strategies would be helpful to calculate the missing value. **SUGGESTED QUESTIONS:** • What do you need to do to find out the median? • How do you know that that is the missing value? • Is there anything that you could do to check? **Beijing 2008** The data shows the results from the Olympic Games for 2008. Websites and other resources for the Games give a wealth of data for different sports, many of which the children may have seen. The data presented in the table gives fractions of a second. Talk about how the lowest number in a race is the best result. **SUGGESTED QUESTIONS:** • How many athletes were faster than 10 seconds? • What was the difference in time between the runner who came first and the runner who came last?	Interpreting data	126 127
Shady business More likely: 1 and 2	**Handling data** Describe and predict outcomes from data using the language of chance or likelihood	**Shady business** This activity uses spinners as a resource to generate data about chance. Blank spinners are best copied onto card. Ensure that the children cut along the edges carefully so as not to affect which side the spinner lands on. Supervision might be needed when making the hole through the centre of the spinner. **SUGGESTED QUESTIONS:** • Why do you think that spinner is more likely to land on the shaded part? • Can you shade the spinner so that it is twice as likely to land on blue than on red? **More likely: 1 and 2** How to play the game ☆ In pairs or in small groups, the children cut out and shuffle the cards from pages 19 and 20. ☆ One player deals the cards so that each player has an equal number of cards. ☆ Each player places their cards in a pile face down on the table. ☆ Players turn over their top card and the player with the card that describes a 'more likely' event keeps the cards. If two events are equally likely, the cards are placed in the middle and picked up by the winner of the next round. ☆ The player with the most cards at the end of the game wins. The children could add to the cards for this game by writing their own scenarios. The content is based on calculable outcomes, rather than likelihood – this could be the content of another game. The game cards could be copied onto thin card and laminated. As this game is intended to promote discussion, ensure that the children are free to challenge their opponent(s) – especially if mixed-ability children are working together. **SUGGESTED QUESTIONS:** • Explain why that situation is mathematically more probable than this one. • Can you give me a situation that would be as equally likely as the one on this card?	Interpreting data	128 129–130
Measurement bingo	**Measuring** Select and use standard metric units of measure and convert between units using decimals to two places (e.g. change 2.75 litres to 2750 ml, or vice versa)	**Measurement bingo** Once the children have filled in measurements onto a bingo board, call out any of the following measures or their equivalents: 120cm 0.3kg 5500m 2.5l 3700ml 90mm 1240g 5.5cm 0.25kg 3000g 9cm 0.37l 0.78m 2800ml 4l 0.75kg 45cm 40cm 3.7km 1.5m 119mm 700g 325cm 0.68kg 220g 5000m 2mm 2.73km **SUGGESTED PROMPT/QUESTIONS:** • Tell me a different measure we could use for 150cm. • Which is the shortest length on your bingo board? What would the length be in a different unit?	Measures	131
Arrow error	**Measuring** Read and interpret scales on a range of measuring instruments, recognising that the measurement made is approximate and recording results to a required degree of accuracy; compare readings on different scales, for example when using different instruments	**Arrow error** At the start of the lesson, revise the conversion of kilograms to grams by saying an amount in kilograms, for example 1.2kg, and asking the children to write the amount in grams. **SUGGESTED QUESTIONS:** • How did you know this scale was incorrect? • How could you show 75 g on the scales?	Measures	132

Activity name	Strand and learning objectives	Notes on the activities	Assessment Focus	Page number
Patrick's patterns Model thinking	**Using and applying mathematics** Solve multi-step problems, and problems involving fractions, decimals and percentages; choose and use appropriate calculation strategies at each stage, including calculator use	**Patrick's patterns** *Processes: visualise, reason, make decisions, look for pattern, be systematic* The lengths of the initial shapes could be changed to provide more variety or differentiation. **Suggested question:** • Can you show me what you did? **Model thinking** *Processes: visualise, reason, make decisions, look for pattern, be systematic* This worksheet can be used as a follow-on from the previous worksheet. As a further extension, the children could sketch their own models for others to find related lengths. **Suggested questions:** • How can you be sure that this is the correct length? • What did you do?	Problem solving	133 134
Dragon trail	**Calculating** Calculate mentally with integers and decimals: U.t ± U.t, TU × U, TU ÷ U, U.t × U, U.t ÷ U	**Dragon trail** You could use a timer and ask the children to see how many questions they can answer in a set time, for example within three minutes. When children are tackling the extension activity, remind them that they can use the test for divisibility by 3 to help them. **Suggested questions:** • What method did you use to work out 85 ÷ 6? • How could you check your answer to 93 ÷ 5?	Mental methods	135
Shopping parade	**Calculating** Use efficient written methods to add and subtract integers and decimals, to multiply and divide integers and decimals by a one-digit integer, and to multiply two-digit and three-digit integers by a two-digit integer	**Shopping parade** For those children who are not confident in dealing with decimals, ask them to convert the amount of money from pounds to pence, where appropriate, and then to perform the multiplication, before converting back to pounds at the end. **Suggested prompt/question:** • Explain how you worked out the answer. • Show me your written method of multiplication.	Written methods	136
Best estimate	**Measuring** Select and use standard metric units of measure and convert between units using decimals to two places (e.g. change 2.75 litres to 2750 ml, or vice versa)	**Best estimate** At the start of the lesson ask the children to list all the units of measure that they know. Discuss the relationships between the different units for a particular measure, for example 1 m = 100cm, 1 cm = 10mm. **Suggested questions/prompts:** • What units could you use to measure area, mass, capacity? • Estimate the length of this classroom, the school hall, the width of the playground.	Measures	137
Measure up: 1 and 2	**Measuring** Read and interpret scales on a range of measuring instruments, recognising that the measurement made is approximate and recording results to a required degree of accuracy; compare readings on different scales, for example when using different instruments	**Measure up: 1 and 2** Demonstrate how to count the number of intervals between two numbered positions on the scale and to divide the difference between the two numbers by the number of intervals, for example there are five intervals between 0 and 10, and 10 ÷ 5 = 2, so each interval has a value of 2ml. **Suggested questions:** • How do you know that the total of the three containers is 74ml? • How would you show 35ml on this measuring cylinder?	Measures	138–139
Perimeter patterns Rectangular reasoning	**Measuring** Calculate the perimeter and area of rectilinear shapes; estimate the area of an irregular shape by counting squares	**Perimeter patterns** This activity encourages the children to reason about the lengths of unknown sides. **Suggested questions:** • How did you work out the perimeter of this shape? • Which shapes have the same perimeters? Why do you think this is? **Rectangular reasoning** When exploring the concept of area it is vital that it is the children's attention is focused on the number of squares inside the shape rather than just on the length and the width of the rectangle. By providing lots of experience of counting squares the children will begin to appreciate that this can be speeded up by finding how many rows of squares there are and how many squares are in each row. Multiplication can then be used. This sheet can be used for either area or perimeter or for both. Write 'perimeter', 'area' or 'perimeter and area' into the box. If the children are being asked to find the area, demonstrate how to split the shape up into rectangles (note that there is generally more than one way that this can be done) and to find the areas of the rectangles and then the total area. **Suggested questions:** • How can you draw a rectangular shape with a perimeter of 80cm? • How can you draw a rectangular shape with an area of 80cm²?	Measures	140 141

Block D Calculating, measuring and understanding shape Unit 2

Activity name	Strand and learning objectives	Notes on the activities	Assessment Focus	Page number
Rocky's wall and rockery	**Using and applying mathematics** Solve multi-step problems, and problems involving fractions, decimals and percentages; choose and use appropriate calculation strategies at each stage, including calculator use	**Rocky's wall and rockery** *Processes: reason, explain, record, visualise, make decisions, check* These problems require the children to make their own decisions as to how to answer the questions. When giving answers as fractions, encourage the children to give them in their simplest forms. **SUGGESTED QUESTIONS:** • How did you find the answer?	Problem solving	142
Nutrition numbers	**Calculating** Calculate mentally with integers and decimals: U.t ± U.t, TU × U, TU ÷ U, U.t × U, U.t ÷ U	**Nutrition numbers** For homework, the children could use real food labels to make up similar questions of their own. **SUGGESTED QUESTIONS:** • Did you partition the decimal? • Did you work out a whole number answer and then divide by 10? • What method of multiplication did you use?	Mental methods	143
Revolution solutions	**Measuring** Estimate angles and use a protractor to measure and draw them, on their own and in shapes.	**Revolution solution** This more challenging angle activity involves children identifying angles in squares and triangles and then using the information to find angles about a point. Begin the lesson by showing examples such as these: $360° – 90° – 90° – 90° = 90°$ $360° – 60° – 60° – 60° – 60° = 120°$ **SUGGESTED PROMPT/QUESTION:** • Explain how you worked out the size of the marked angle. • How could you check your answers?	Measures	144
Micro dominoes	**Measuring** Select and use standard metric units of measure and convert between units using decimals to two places (e.g. change 2.75 litres to 2750 ml, or vice versa)	**Micro dominoes** Remind the children of the relationships between metric units of measure and practise converting between them at the start of this lesson. Children will require scissors and glue for this activity. **SUGGESTED QUESTION/PROMPT:** • How did you know that these two dominoes match? • I have a domino that has 3 cm on it. Tell me two measures that could match to it.	Measures	145
Angle tangle They do, duvet? Get to the point	**Measuring** Estimate angles, and use a protractor to measure and draw them, on their own and in shapes; calculate angles in a triangle or around a point	**Angle tangle** Children will require rulers and protractors for this activity. Demonstrate how to use a protractor or angle measurer at the start of the lesson. Ensure the children realise that there is often more than one position that the protractor can be placed in, to make a correct reading. Explain how to read a protractor to the nearest degree. When the children have joined the dots in order they will find that the letters mark the angles formed. They then estimate and measure these angles and record them in the grid. Most children should record their answers to the nearest degree. Children who find this activity difficult could read the protractors to the nearest 5 degrees. **SUGGESTED QUESTIONS:** • Is this angle larger than this angle? • Is this angle larger or smaller than a right angle? • How could you check to find out? • About how many degrees do you think this angle is? • Is the angle acute or obtuse? **They do, duvet?** For higher attaining children, mask the following angles so that they use their knowledge not only that angles in a triangle add to 180° but also that the corners of the duvet add to make 90°, the angles along a straight line add to make 180° and angles about a point have a total of 360°. **SUGGESTED QUESTIONS:** • Is the missing angle acute or obtuse? • What calculation did you use to work out the size of the missing angle? How can you check that your answer is correct? **Get to the point** At the start of the lesson, discuss the fact that the angles about a point add to make 360°. Provide some practice in using addition and subtraction from 360° to find missing angles. Some children could be given a calculator if appropriate. If the angles are ordered correctly from largest to smallest, the letters spell out the sentence 'COLOUR ALL THE REFLEX ANGLES YELLOW.' It may be necessary to explain what a reflex angle is to enable them to follow the instruction. **SUGGESTED QUESTIONS:** • Is the missing angle acute or obtuse? • What calculation did you use to work out the size of the missing angle? How can you check that your answer is correct?	Measures	146 147 148
Coded coordinates Coordinate puzzles	**Understanding shape** Use coordinates in the first quadrant to draw, locate and complete shapes that meet given properties	**Coded coordinates** Children often find it difficult to visualise shapes represented on grids in different orientations. This activity helps the children to begin to explore and visualise such shapes, given their vertices. It also provides opportunity for practising plotting points correctly using coordinates. **SUGGESTED QUESTIONS:** • Why do you think that A, F, H and B could be the vertices of a square? • Tell me the coordinates of another scalene triangle that you could make from these points. **Coordinate puzzles** More practice in locating vertices of shapes is given on this worksheet. The children could work together in pairs, if preferred. Different answers are possible for the puzzles on this worksheet. Discuss all the possible solutions that the children have found for each question. **SUGGESTED PROMPTS/QUESTIONS:** • It is possible to make another isosceles triangle that has these two points as two of its vertices. Where could the other vertex be to make a different isosceles triangle to yours? • I want to draw an equilateral triangle on this grid. The vertices have to be points on the grid. Is this possible? Why not?	Properties of position and movement	149 150

Activity name	Strand and learning objectives	Notes on the activities	Assessment Focus	Page number
Reflection selection	**Understanding shape** Visualise and draw on grids of different types where a shape will be after reflection, after translations, or after rotation through 90° or 180° about its centre or one of its vertices	**Reflection selection** Strategies for reflection include turning the page so that each mirror line is vertical, and counting from each vertex perpendicularly to the mirror line and beyond to mark the new vertex. The patterns in the coordinates when reflection is in the line y = x is interesting because each y-coordinate swaps place with each x-coordinate to produce the reflection. Encourage the children to notice this pattern for themselves. As an extension, the children could draw their own coordinate grids on squared paper and design their own shapes and their reflections. Once the rule is known, the children can create quite complex patterns. **SUGGESTED QUESTIONS:** • What do you notice about the coordinates of these two points? • What do the numbers have in common? **Rotation station: 1 and 2** These worksheets provide practice in plotting the vertices of shapes and joining them before then rotating them through 90° or 180° about a vertex or its centre. **SUGGESTED QUESTIONS:** • What do you notice about the lengths of the sides of the original shape and the lengths of the sides of the rotated shapes in the new positions? • What can you say about a rotation of 180° clockwise and a rotation of 180° anticlockwise about the same point?	Properties of position and movement	151
Rotation station: 1 and 2				152–153

Block D Calculating, measuring and understanding shape Unit 3

Activity name	Strand and learning objectives	Notes on the activities	Assessment Focus	Page number
Dimitri's day	**Using and applying mathematics** Solve multi-step problems, and problems involving fractions, decimals and percentages; choose and use appropriate calculation strategies at each stage, including calculator use	**Dimitri's day** *Processes: reason, explain, record, visualise, make decisions* This worksheet involves calculating time events. **SUGGESTED QUESTIONS:** • How did you find the answer?	Problem solving	154
Scale drawings	**Calculating** Calculate mentally with integers and decimals: U.t ± U.t, TU × U, TU ÷ U, U.t × U, U.t ÷ U	**Scale drawings** The children will require rulers for this activity. Encourage them to measure accurately to the nearest tenth of a centimetre and to write the lengths as decimals. **SUGGESTED QUESTIONS:** • How did you work out the answer to 5.6 ÷ 4? What multiplication facts did you use to help you? **Gemstone necklace** Children use trial and improvement methods to work out what each gem stands for. Encourage them to think about what the size of the difference	Mental methods	155
Gemstone necklace		says about how close the numbers are, and so how close to or far from half of the total each number must be. For example, in the first question, the difference between the gem numbers is nearly half the size of the total. So the smaller number must be about a quarter the size of the total. Also, if the children add the result of the addition to the result of the subtraction this sum is exactly double the larger of the two numbers. **SUGGESTED QUESTION:** • Can you explain how you worked out the missing numbers?		156
Erin's errors	**Calculating** Use efficient written methods to add and subtract integers and decimals, to multiply and divide integers and decimals by a one-digit integer, and to multiply two-digit and three-digit integers by a two-digit integer	**Erin's errors** Provide the children with a coloured pen or pencil to mark this work and ask them to talk to a partner about where Erin went wrong in each calculation. Where an error was made early in the calculation, the consequential steps will also contain errors. If preferred, you could ask the children to write out the calculation correctly on a separate piece of paper, rather than annotating the worksheet. **SUGGESTED QUESTIONS:** • Why do you think Erin made this error? • Have you ever made an error like this?	Written methods	157
Time after time	**Calculating** Use a calculator to solve problems involving multi-step calculations	**Time after time** Encourage the children to talk about how they might solve each problem and remind them how to convert between hours, minutes and seconds by multiplying or dividing by 60. **SUGGESTED QUESTIONS:** • How did you answer this question? • What did you key into the calculator?	Solving numerical methods	158
Quick conversions	**Measuring** Select and use standard metric units of measure and convert between units using decimals to two places (e.g. change 2.75 litres to 2750 ml, or vice versa)	**Quick conversions** At the start of the lesson, practise multiplying and dividing by 10, 100 and 1000. **SUGGESTED PROMPT:** • Explain how you worked out the answer.	Measures	159

Activity name	Strand and learning objectives	Notes on the activities	Assessment Focus	Page number
Full scale ahead	**Measuring** Read and interpret scales on a range of measuring instruments, recognising that the measurement made is approximate and recording results to a required degree of accuracy; compare readings on different scales, for example when using different instruments	**Full scale ahead** This activity encourages the children to appreciate that measurement is approximate and that it is important to know the degree of accuracy to which you are recording a reading. **SUGGESTED QUESTION/PROMPT:** • What is that measurement to the nearest 1 kg? • Draw an arrow to show 43 kg on this scale. **Rubber sizes** Demonstrate how the children will have to make three readings for each question: a) the inner edge of the first grey line, b) the inner edge of the other grey line and c) the point at which the rubbers meet. Discuss how the children can use these measurements to work out the length of each rubber. (Rubber 1 is the difference between a and c, and rubber 2 is the difference between b and c.) Note that these measurements are to the nearest millimetre. **SUGGESTED QUESTION:** • Can you explain how to find the length of this rubber?	Measures	160
Rubber sizes			Measures	161
Half squares	**Measuring** Calculate the perimeter and area of rectilinear shapes; estimate the area of an irregular shape by counting squares	**Half squares** Provide the children with squared paper for the extension activity. **SUGGESTED QUESTION:** • Can you make a shape with an area of 8 cm²? **Something fishy** At the start of the lesson, revise how to find the areas of irregular shapes by counting squares. Discuss how to decide which squares and half squares to count and which to discount. **SUGGESTED QUESTION:** • Which other fish has approximately the same area as this one? **Carpet calculations** Some children may find this activity challenging without support. Discuss suitable strategies for finding the areas of the rooms and then using multiplication to find the cost of the carpets for each room. Provide the children with a calculator for this task. The realities of carpet fitting could also be discussed, where offcuts are paid for. This would mean that the area of carpet for the kitchen would need to be a rectangle and the corner piece would need to be cut out. **SUGGESTED QUESTIONS:** • What is the area of this room? • How much carpet will be needed?	Measures	162
Something fishy				163
Carpet calculations				164

Block E Securing number facts, calculating, identifying relationships Unit 1

Activity name	Strand and learning objectives	Notes on the activities	Assessment Focus	Page number
Fun at the fair	**Using and applying mathematics** Tabulate systematically the information in a problem or puzzle; identify and record the steps or calculations needed to solve it, using symbols where appropriate; interpret solutions in the original context and check their accuracy	**Fun at the fair** *Processes: reason, test ideas, be systematic, look for pattern, trial and improvement, check* As the children tackle these problems, encourage them to say what patterns or clues they are looking for to help them solve the puzzles. Draw attention to any children who use a table format or list of coins to help them. **SUGGESTED QUESTIONS/PROMPT:** • How did you find the answer? • What patterns did you look for? • Explain how you solved these problems. **Dancing dilemma** *Processes: explain, reason, compare, visualise* Allow the children to organise the information in their own way, but draw attention to good strategies involving a systematic approach. **SUGGESTED QUESTIONS:** • How did you organise the information? • What did you write down? • How did you know that he wasn't dancing? • What did this clue tell you?	Reasoning	165
Dancing dilemma				166
Talking points: 1 and 2	**Using and applying mathematics** Explain reasoning and conclusions, using words, symbols or diagrams as appropriate	**Talking points: 1 and 2** *Processes: look for pattern, test ideas, reason, generalise, hypothesise* Explain that the original number need not always be a whole number. **SUGGESTED QUESTIONS:** • Can you explain how you worked this out? • Do you agree? • Is this always true? • How can you be sure?	Communicating	167–168
Farming fractions	**Using and applying mathematics** Solve multi-step problems, and problems involving fractions, decimals and percentages; choose and use appropriate calculation strategies at each stage, including calculator use	**Farming fractions** *Processes: reason, make decisions, explain, generalise, trial and improvement, visualise, test ideas, look for pattern* Focus on the children describing how they went about tackling this activity, and help them to begin to generalise strategies for any questions of this type, for example by converting all fractions to those with the same denominator and then subtracting them from one to find what fraction the number of goats represents. This can then help them to find the total number of animals and thus the number of each type. To simplify the activity for lower attaining children, change the numbers in the questions: field A: change all the fractions to $\frac{1}{4}$ (total number of animals becomes 20); field B: change the fraction that are cows to $\frac{1}{10}$ and the fraction that are sheep to $\frac{3}{10}$ (total number of animals becomes 10); field C: change the fraction that are horses to $\frac{1}{5}$, and the fraction that are sheep to $\frac{2}{5}$ (total number of animals becomes 95). **Copy cats** Ask the children to describe how to calculate percentages of numbers or quantities in their heads and using jottings. Some children may need a calculator for the more difficult calculations, particularly in the extension activity. **SUGGESTED QUESTIONS/PROMPT:** • What method of calculation did you use? • Did you use a mental, written, or calculator method? • Can you show me what you did? • Make up some more percentage changes of your own and alter the picture size.	Problem solving	169
Copy cats				170

Activity name	Strand and learning objectives	Notes on the activities		Assessment Focus	Page number
Planet exploration	**Calculating** Use efficient written methods to add and subtract integers and decimals, to multiply and divide integers and decimals by a one-digit integer, and to multiply two-digit and three-digit integers by a two-digit integer	**Planet exploration** Discuss suitable strategies for multiplying decimals using written methods, for example by multiplying two whole numbers and adjusting the answer at the end (37×0.8 could be found by multiplying 37 by 8 and then dividing the answer by 10). Encourage the children who tackle the extension activity to be sensitive about the weight of other children. If weighing scales are not available, the children could estimate their weight.	For more of a challenge, the numbers on the worksheet can be made more accurate, for example: Mercury 0.28, Venus 0.91, Uranus 0.79, Mars 0.38, Neptune 1.12, Jupiter 2.34. **Suggested question/prompt:** • How did you set out the multiplication? • Show me what you did.	Written methods	171
Pack it in How are we related? Fraction quiz A sure measure	**Counting and understanding number** Express a larger whole number as a fraction of a smaller one (e.g. recognise that 8 slices of a 5-slice pizza represents $\frac{8}{5}$ or $1\frac{3}{5}$ pizzas); simplify fractions by cancelling common factors; order a set of fractions by converting them to fractions with a common denominator	**Pack it in** At the start of the lesson, revise the meanings of 'improper fraction', 'mixed number', 'denominator' and 'numerator'. Check that children understand that the phrase 'what fraction of a 6-pack of yoghurt is 7 pots?' means 'what fraction do we write when we have 7 lots of one-sixth?' **Suggested questions:** What fraction of a 6-pack of yoghurts is 5 pots? How is that fraction different to all your answers on the page? **How are we related?** This activity is good to play as a classroom activity, once children are confident in expressing one number as a fraction of another. Give each child in the room a number card to hold. Ask the children to move around the room and, as they meet people, to say what fraction of the other person's number their own is, for example: 'My number is $\frac{9}{10}$ of your number' or 'My number is $1\frac{1}{9}$ times your number'. To assist the children with this skill, point out that their number will always be the numerator and the other child's number will be the denominator. If their number is larger, they should try to convert the improper fraction to a mixed number.	**Suggested questions:** • What fraction of £10 is £4? • What fraction of £4 is £10? How could you say this as a mixed number? **Fraction quiz** Ensure the children appreciate that there may be more than one correct answer for the quiz questions. **Suggested question/prompt:** • Show me how you worked that out. • What fraction of the whole week is the weekend? **A sure measure** In this activity, the children have to express their answers in the simplest form. Before they complete the questions on the worksheet, practise simplifying proper fractions, for example $\frac{35}{70}$, $\frac{28}{100}$ and $\frac{63}{72}$. **Suggested questions:** • How could you simplify this fraction further? • What is this improper fraction as a mixed number?	Fractions, decimals, percentages, ratio and proportion	172 173 174 175
Sorting session Fraction satisfaction	**Calculating** Relate fractions to multiplication and division (e.g. $6 \div 2 = \frac{1}{2}$ of $6 = 6 \times \frac{1}{2}$); express a quotient as a fraction or decimal (e.g. $67 \div 5 = 13.4$ or $13\frac{2}{5}$); find fractions and percentages of whole-number quantities (e.g. $\frac{5}{8}$ of 96, 65% of £260)	**Sorting session** At the start of the lesson, discuss the different ways of presenting the question '18 divided by 4', for example: $18 \div 4$, $\frac{1}{4}$ of 18, $18 \times \frac{1}{4}$, $\frac{18}{4}$. If preferred, the children could work in pairs for this activity. **Suggested questions:** • What known multiplication facts did you use to help you work out that answer? • How could you write that calculation as a division? **Fraction satisfaction** When finding fractions of numbers, encourage the children to first find the unit fraction of the number by dividing by the denominator,	for example for $\frac{3}{4}$ of 160, finding $\frac{1}{4}$ first by dividing by 4 and then finally multiplying by 3 to find $\frac{3}{4}$ of the number. **Suggested prompts/questions:** • Explain to me how you worked out the fractions of these numbers. • Did you divide first? By which number? Why? • Does it matter in which order you multiply or divide? Try it.	Fractions, decimals, percentages, ratio and proportion	176 177
Hens and chicks 'Coven' Garden Market	**Counting and understanding number** Solve simple problems involving direct proportion by scaling quantities up or down	**Hens and chicks** Encourage the children to cover the unused part of the ratio diagram with a book or hand when they are answering the questions. **Suggested questions:** • How many chicks are in the yard if there are 24 hens? • How could you work this out quickly without using the diagram?	**'Coven' Garden Market** Remind the children to look at whether the prices are given in pounds or pence to ensure that they give the correct unit in their answers. **Suggested questions:** • How much will five spider webs cost if two cost 60p? • Which of these calculations did you find most difficult? Why?	Fractions, decimals, percentages, ratio and proportion	178 179

Block E Securing number facts, calculating, identifying relationships Unit 2

Activity name	Strand and learning objectives	Notes on the activities		Assessment Focus	Page number
Eggs-ibition Puzzle patterns	**Using and applying mathematics** Tabulate systematically the information in a problem or puzzle; identify and record the steps or calculations needed to solve it, using symbols where appropriate; interpret solutions in the original context and check their accuracy	**Eggs-ibition** *Processes: visualise, be systematic, explain* Encourage the children to organise their solutions into groups. **Suggested question:** • Why did you choose to draw these six solutions? There are 30 solutions: 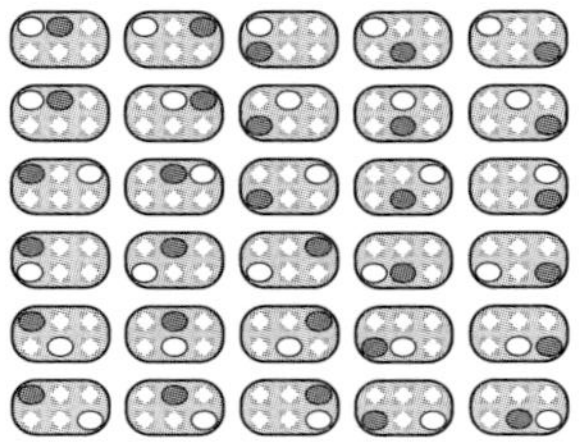	**Puzzle patterns** *Processes: explain, reason, look for pattern* The children should work in pairs for this activity so that they can discuss strategies. These four problems can be solved using the same strategy. Encourage the children to realise this for themselves, rather than telling them. As an extension, ask the children to make up another problem that is similar to the ones on the page, and to show the calculations they would use to answer it. **Suggested questions:** • How did you find the answers? • Can you explain to the others what you noticed? • What is similar about these four questions? • Can you make up a fifth question that is also similar?	Reasoning	180 181

Activity name	Strand and learning objectives	Notes on the activities	Assessment Focus	Page number
How did you work it out?	**Using and applying mathematics** Explain reasoning and conclusions, using words, symbols or diagrams as appropriate	**How did you work it out?** Processes: *explain, reason, record, justify, test ideas, trial and improvement* This activity encourages the children to describe the strategies they would use to solve a problem, and to consider the different ways that this could be done. **Suggested questions:** • What would you do? • Would you use a mental or written method? • What strategies did you use? • What other ways could it be done?	Communicating	182
Percentage rocket race	**Calculating** Use a calculator to solve problems involving multi-step calculations	**Percentage rocket race** The children play this game in pairs – a third child could act as adjudicator. The children will each need a counter, a calculator and a piece of scrap paper on which to keep their own scores, and one copy of the sheet and a dice to share. This game requires the children to enter the questions into a calculator and to keep score. **Suggested prompt/questions:** • Explain to me how you worked out the percentages of these numbers.	Solving numerical problems	183
Extreme sports		**Extreme sports** For each question, encourage the children to check that the total prize money given as answers matches that in the question. **Suggested questions:** • What fraction could you use to find 75% of an amount? • When finding 10% of an amount, what can you divide by?		184
Domino loop	**Counting and understanding number** Express a larger whole number as a fraction of a smaller one (e.g. recognise that 8 slices of a 5-slice pizza represents $\frac{8}{5}$ or $1\frac{3}{5}$ pizzas); simplify fractions by cancelling common factors; order a set of fractions by converting them to fractions with a common denominator	**Domino loop** These dominoes could be enlarged onto A3, copied and then laminated for a more permanent resource. **Suggested questions:** • What is this improper fraction as a mixed number? • What is the denominator of this number? • How many fifths are there in one-whole/two-wholes?	Fractions, decimals, percentages, ratio and proportion	185
Robot twins		**Robot twins** Check that the children simplify the fractions to the smallest denominator possible. For some of the fractions (for example $\frac{5}{20}$ $\frac{18}{54}$ $\frac{36}{48}$ and $\frac{45}{90}$), it is possible to divide the denominator by the numerator. **Suggested questions:** • Which number did you divide the numerator and the denominator by?		186
I scream for ice-cream		**I scream for ice-cream** The extension activity asks the children to find fractions of 40 and then simplify the result. As a further extension, the children can investigate what happens when they find what fraction of 80 or 120 each number is. **Suggested questions:** • Which number did you divide the numerator and the denominator by? • Is there another number you could divide them by? • Is this fraction in its simplest form?		187
Percentage code	**Counting and understanding number** Express one quantity as a percentage of another (e.g. express £400 as a percentage of £1000); find equivalent percentages, decimals and fractions	**Percentage code** This activity can help children to appreciate that more than one fraction can convert to the same percentage. In this example, several different fractions convert to 24%. Draw the children's attention to this fact once the worksheet is completed. As an extension, ask the children to make up their own percentage code for a partner to solve. **Suggested questions/prompt:** • What number do you need to multiply by to go from 20 to 100? • Now multiply the numerator by this number. • How would you write this fraction as a percentage? **gBay** At the start of the lesson, check that the children understand what is meant by the percentage rating, and why sellers and buyers might find it useful. Would they want to buy from someone with a rating of 23%?	Fractions, decimals, percentages, ratio and proportion	188
gBay		**Suggested questions:** • How could you work out different scores that would give a rating of 85%? • Can you explain to a partner what you would do?		189
Cat and mouse		**Cat and mouse** This activity can help children to begin to recognise fractions, decimals and percentages of the same value, without the need to work out the equivalents. **Suggested questions:** • Which fraction is equivalent to 0.6? • What is the value of the digit to the right of the decimal point? • How do you convert a decimal into a percentage?		190
Book boxes	**Calculating** Relate fractions to multiplication and division (e.g. $6 \div 2 = \frac{1}{2}$ of 6 = $6 \times \frac{1}{2}$); express a quotient as a fraction or decimal (e.g. $67 \div 5 = 13.4$ or $13\frac{2}{5}$); find fractions and percentages of whole-number quantities (e.g. $\frac{5}{8}$ of 96, 65% of £260)	**Book boxes** This context provides children with an appreciation of a remainder being given as a fraction, rather than as a remainder. **Suggested questions/prompt:** • How did you work out this answer? • How could this remainder be written as a fraction? Write the divisor as the denominator of the fraction.	Fractions, decimals, percentages, ratio and proportion	191
Quotient quiz		**Quotient quiz** Discuss situations where it is most appropriate to give the answer to a division as a decimal, for example when cutting measured lengths into equal pieces. **Suggested questions:** • Which method did you use to work out 93 ÷ 6? • Did you use the same method or a different one to work out 99.5? Why?		192
Fraction-packed shapes		**Fraction-packed shapes** At the start of the activity, check that the children remember that there are 10 mm in 1cm. For your reference, the sizes of the original shapes are as follows: 1 75mm² 2 64mm × 80mm 3 72mm × 45mm 4 85mm × 40mm 5 156mm × 55mm		193
Percentage strip		As a further extension, the children could draw a circle within the smallest circle, with a diameter of the previous circle (diameter would be 9cm). **Suggested questions:** • How did you work out what the length of that side should be? • If you work out two-fifths of a length is, how can you work out what three-fifths is? **Percentage strip** This tool can be very useful for helping children to gain an understanding of how percentages of quantities and numbers can be found. Demonstrate how the shaded boxes can be filled in first, for example finding 50% by halving the number, 10% by dividing it by 10 and so on, and then show how other percentages can be built up using those that are known. **Suggested prompt:** • How did you work out the percentages of these numbers?		194

Activity name	Strand and learning objectives	Notes on the activities	Assessment Focus	Page number
Great grams	**Counting and understanding number** Solve simple problems involving direct proportion by scaling quantities up or down	**Great grams** This activity involves children scaling up or down to solve direct proportion questions. Encourage the children to discuss the methods that could be used to solve this type of problem, for example to find the cost per gram and then multiply, or they could work out the fraction of 100 g (for example 2½ times larger) and then multiply the price accordingly. Give the children the opportunity to try a variety of methods and to say which approach they prefer. **SUGGESTED PROMPT:** • Show me how you worked out how many grams were bought.	Fractions, decimals, percentages, ratio and proportion	195

Block E Securing number facts, calculating, identifying relationships Unit 3

Activity name	Strand and learning objectives	Notes on the activities	Assessment Focus	Page number
A matter of balance: 1 and 2	**Using and applying mathematics** Tabulate systematically the information in a problem or puzzle; identify and record the steps or calculations needed to solve it, using symbols where appropriate; interpret solutions in the original context and check their accuracy	**A matter of balance: 1 and 2** *Processes: visualise, make decisions, reason, be systematic* These worksheets can be used to help the children visualise simple equations and to begin to understand how to solve them. By representing each picture as an equation, the children can begin to understand the relationship between the items on the scales and an abstract equation. Firstly, allow the children to tackle the worksheets themselves and then ask them to explain what they did to work out the problems. Some children may have chosen to use a simple equation idea, perhaps using shapes or pictures as symbols. **SUGGESTED QUESTIONS:** • How did you find this solution? • Can you explain what you did or wrote down? • Can you see how I have written an equation? • What do you think m stands for? • How could we use the equation to help us work this out?	Reasoning	196–197
Gas bill changes 'Expert' deals Courgette croquettes	**Using and applying mathematics** Solve multi-step problems, and problems involving fractions, decimals and percentages; choose and use appropriate calculation strategies at each stage, including calculator use	**Gas bill changes** *Processes: reason, explain, look for pattern, generalise, check* Remind the children of ways to increase or reduce numbers or quantities by percentages, for example by finding the percentage amount and then adding or subtracting it. Children (and sometimes adults) often believe that an increase and then a decrease of the same size returns the amount to its original value. Discuss with the children that, because the second percentage is of the new amount, this is not true. **SUGGESTED QUESTIONS/PROMPT:** • Can you explain how you answered this using a number sentence? • Did you use a mental, written, or calculator method? • What do you notice about the percentages? • Are you surprised? Explain why. **'Expert' deals** *Processes: reason, make decisions, look for pattern, generalise, check* This worksheet leads on from the previous activity and encourages the children to appreciate that the order of making percentage changes is unimportant. Ensure, however, that the children do not merely add the percentages together to make a 35% discount, as after each discount is taken the new amount is less and therefore the percentage discount acts on a smaller value each time. Provide calculators for this activity and encourage the children to discuss the patterns they notice and to reason and explain them. As a further extension, the children could be asked to find the overall percentage discount: 31.6%. **SUGGESTED QUESTIONS:** • How did you find this solution? • How much would you save? **Courgette croquettes** *Processes: reason, record, explain, compare, check* To simplify the activity: – delete 200 from breadcrumbs and write in 1000 for the courgettes; – change the statement about courgettes and onions to 'The mass of the onions is one-quarter of the mass of the courgettes'; – change the statement about the breadcrumbs and the potatoes to 'The mass of the potatoes is 2 times the mass of the breadcrumbs.' The children will need to use a calculator for the extension activity. **SUGGESTED QUESTIONS:** • How did you tackle these questions? • Can you write a calculation to show what you did?	Problem solving	198 199 200
Division decisions	**Number facts and calculations** Use knowledge of place value and multiplication facts to 10 × 10 to derive related multiplication and division facts involving decimals (e.g. 0.8 × 7, 4.8 ÷ 6)	**Division decisions** Children will require scissors and glue for this activity. Provide each child with a copy of the sheet and ask them to fit the small hexagons into the centres of the larger ones so that each division has been correctly answered. If necessary, make these activities a little simpler, ask the children to start with the larger hexagons and to answer the questions, writing the answers in the centre of the large hexagons. The children can then find the matching small hexagons showing the same answers. **SUGGESTED QUESTION:** • Which tables and related division facts could you use to help you answer this division?	Mental methods	201
Precision division Division patterns	**Calculating** Use efficient written methods to add and subtract integers and decimals, to multiply and divide integers and decimals by a one-digit integer, and to multiply two-digit and three-digit integers by a two-digit integer	**Precision division** This activity helps children begin to divide numbers using partitioning methods that lead towards the traditional short division method. The children are encouraged to partition numbers into a multiple of 10 that is divisible by the divisor. **SUGGESTED QUESTION:** • Which method do you find easier? **Division patterns** At the start of the lesson, hold up decimal numbers and ask the children to show the number multiplied or divided by 10. Then show a decimal number, for example 23.6, and ask the children how they could turn it into 236 (multiply by 10). Write a calculation like 23.6 ÷ 4 on the board. Ask the children to suggest a calculation they could use to help them answer it. Invite volunteers to show how they would work out the answer, for example use 236 ÷ 4. Discuss how the children have to be careful to put the decimal point back into the answer. How do they decide where it goes? **SUGGESTED QUESTIONS:** • How did you work out this answer? • Did you use partitioning?	Written methods	202 203

Activity name	Strand and learning objectives	Notes on the activities	Assessment Focus	Page number
Soiled goods	**Calculating** Use a calculator to solve problems involving multi-step calculations	**Soiled goods** At the start of the lesson, recap how to find percentages of amounts. Invite the children to explain how to use a calculator to work out these percentages. They could write or draw the keys that should be pressed to work out 32% of £3.84. Discuss how to round the answer to the nearest whole pence. **Suggested questions:** • How did you decide whether to round your answer up or down? • How can you check that your answers are correct?	Solving numerical problems	204
Fraction line-up Fraction spell Telly addict	**Counting and understanding number** Express a larger whole number as a fraction of a smaller one (e.g. recognise that 8 slices of a 5-slice pizza represents $\frac{8}{5}$ or $1\frac{3}{5}$ pizzas); simplify fractions by cancelling common factors; order a set of fractions by converting them to fractions with a common denominator	**Fraction line-up** At the start of the lesson, demonstrate how the numerator and the denominator of each fraction can be multiplied by a number so that all of the equivalent fractions now have the same denominator. **Suggested questions:** • Have you multiplied or divided both the numerator and the denominator by the same number here? • Are these two fractions equivalent? Which has been written with smaller numbers? • Do all your equivalent fractions now have the same denominator? **Fraction spell** As a further extension, the children could check their answers using a calculator. Show them how the fractions can be converted to decimals by dividing the numerator by the denominator, and then the decimals compared. **Suggested questions:** • Do all your equivalent fractions now help us to order fractions? • How does this approach help us to order fractions? • Is there another way that we could check our answers? **Telly addict** At the start of the lesson, ask the children to list all the pairs of factors of 60. Discuss how this list can help them find equivalents with the denominator 60 of the fractions in the main activity. **Suggested questions:** • How do you know that $\frac{24}{60}$ is equivalent to $\frac{2}{5}$? • $\frac{11}{15}$ is equivalent to $\frac{44}{60}$ so what is $\frac{13}{15}$ equivalent to?	Fractions, decimals, percentages, ratio and proportion	205 206 207
Hoopla stall Colour it!	**Counting and understanding number** Express one quantity as a percentage of another (e.g. express £400 as a percentage of £1000); find equivalent percentages, decimals and fractions	**Hoopla stall** Tell the children that they should be drawing exactly 29 hoops on this worksheet to encourage them to persist in finding all the equivalents. Encourage them to discuss how they might solve these problems. Some children might like to write each percentage as a fraction with a denominator of 100, and then find which fractions are equivalent to this one. Alternatively, the children could convert each given fraction to a percentage, using a calculator if necessary. **Suggested questions:** • How do you know that that fraction is equivalent to that percentage? **Colour it!** This type of question is a common context used in the National Tests for 11 year olds. **Suggested questions:** • How did you work out how many percent that part was of the whole shape? • If I colour purple half of what is unshaded, what percentage would be left unshaded?	Fractions, decimals, percentages, ratio and proportion	208 209
Team work Percentage rally	**Calculating** Relate fractions to multiplication and division (e.g. $6 \div 2 = \frac{1}{2}$ of $6 = 6 \times \frac{1}{2}$), express a quotient as a fraction or decimal (e.g. $67 \div 5 = 13.4$ or $13\frac{2}{5}$); find fractions and percentages of whole-number quantities (e.g. $\frac{5}{8}$ of 96, 65% of £260)	**Team work** This activity encourages the children to think about the most appropriate way of representing a remainder, or whether to round the answer up or down. For example in question 1, they might want to divide the distance from A to B in two so that they can see that to find the distance AB, they have to divide 60 km by three and then double the result. **Suggested questions:** • Which do you think is the most appropriate way of giving the answer? • Is there another way? • Why is a decimal answer the most suitable here? • Why do we need to round up/down in this situation? **Percentage rally** This game follows on nicely from the previous activity. The children play the game in pairs – a third child could act as adjudicator, if desired. The children will each need a counter and a piece of scrap paper on which to make any jottings and to keep their own scores, and one copy of the sheet and a dice to share. **Suggested questions:** • What method did you use to find 75% of £160? • How could you use fractions of amounts to help you find percentages of amounts?	Fractions, decimals, percentages, ratio and proportion	210 211
Are we nearly there? Cooking crisis	**Counting and understanding number** Solve simple problems involving direct proportion by scaling quantities up or down	**Are we nearly there?** Some children might find it useful to draw marks on the diagram to show the relative distances. For example for question 1, they might want to divide the distance from A to B in two to find the soup for nine people. **Suggested question:** • Can you explain to us how you worked out these answers? **Cooking crisis** In this activity, the children should use the times-table facts that they know for numbers to 10 × 10 to help them first divide three-digit numbers by one-digit numbers, and then multiply multiples of 10 by one-digit numbers. **Suggested questions/prompt:** • Explain how you worked out how much cream was needed for the soup for nine people. • Would you need more or less beef if you were making Beef Baldaire for nine people? How much more?	Fractions, decimals, percentages, ratio and proportion	212 213

Cheers!

At a celebration, people clink glasses.
If there are two glasses, there is one clink.
Each person must clink glasses with
every person.

- Investigate how many clinks there will be
  if there are three, four, five or six glasses.

Show your working here.

NOW TRY THIS!

- Can you find a pattern in the numbers that will
  help you to predict how many clinks there will
  be if there are 10, 11 or 12 glasses?

24

Teachers' note It is important that the children are aware that person A clinking with person B is the same as person B clinking with person A, i.e. that it counts as only one clink. Discuss the different ways that the children tackle this investigation, drawing attention to diagrams or tables used to represent or record the information. See the notes on the activity on page 6 for more information about patterns in the numbers.

A Lesson for Every Day
Maths
10–11 Years
© A&C Black

Mount Everest

The data in this table shows the maximum and minimum temperatures in summer and in winter at the Everest Base Camp and at the summit.

	Everest Base Camp	The summit
Summer maximum	25 °C	⁻5 °C
Summer minimum	⁻9 °C	⁻40 °C
Winter maximum	10 °C	⁻19 °C
Winter minimum	⁻30 °C	⁻50 °C

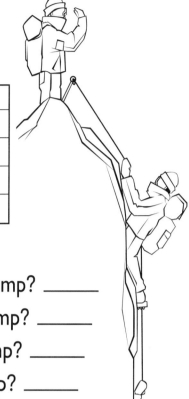

1 How many degrees colder is the:

   a   summer maximum at the summit than at Base Camp? _____

   b   summer minimum at the summit than at Base Camp? _____

   c   winter maximum at the summit than at Base Camp? _____

   d   winter minimum at the summit than at Base Camp? _____

2 At Everest Base Camp, how many degrees colder is the:

   a   winter maximum than the summer maximum? _____

   b   winter minimum than the summer minimum? _____

   c   summer minimum than the summer maximum? _____

   d   winter minimum than the winter maximum? _____

3 At the summit, how many degrees colder is the:

   a   winter maximum than the summer maximum? _____

   b   winter minimum than the summer minimum? _____

   c   summer minimum than the summer maximum? _____

   d   winter minimum than the winter maximum? _____

NOW TRY THIS!

- **Which location has the largest difference in temperature between its summer high and its winter low?** _____
- **What is this difference?** _____

Teachers' note Explain that a difference is not negative, but rather always positive and that it just represents how far apart two numbers or temperatures are.

A Lesson for Every Day
Maths
10–11 Years
© A&C Black

Fly me to the moon

The moon, unlike Earth, does not have an atmosphere so temperatures vary a lot over its surface. Some scientists have placed probes to measure the temperatures at different points on the moon.

	Station 1	Station 2	Station 3	Station 4	Station 5
Night	⁻150 °C	⁻122 °C	⁻100 °C	⁻96 °C	⁻120 °C
Day	90 °C	⁻3 °C	80 °C	⁻96 °C	⁻10 °C

	Station 6	Station 7	Station 8	Station 9	Station 10
Night	⁻170 °C	⁻125 °C	⁻166 °C	⁻157 °C	⁻184 °C
Day	170 °C	0 °C	152 °C	120 °C	214 °C

1 What is the difference between night and day temperatures at:

a Station 7? ___125 °C___   **b** Station 3? _____   **c** Station 1? _____

d Station 6? _____   **e** Station 5? _____   **f** Station 4? _____

g Station 2? _____   **h** Station 10? _____   **i** Station 8? _____

j Station 9? _____

2 Which station's temperature varies:

a the most? _____   **b** the least? _____

3 Find the temperature difference at night between:

a Stations 7 and 3 _____   **b** Stations 3 and 5 _____

c Stations 1 and 10 _____   **d** Stations 6 and 4 _____

e Stations 5 and 2 _____   **f** Stations 2 and 8 _____

g Stations 9 and 1 _____   **h** Stations 10 and 4 _____

NOW TRY THIS!

• **Find stations with a day temperature difference of:**
100 °C   186 °C   173 °C   86 °C   248 °C   310 °C

Teachers' note It could be explained to the children that Station 4 is positioned at one of the poles of the moon, where the temperature remains constant and that Station 10, where the temperature range is largest, is at a point on the 'equator'.

A Lesson for Every Day
Maths
10–11 Years
© A&C Black

I am the champion

- ## Play this game with a partner.

☆ The aim of the game is to 'destroy' all your opponent's 'defences'. Player 1 picks two of player 2's numbers and says the difference between them. If they are correct, they cross out those two numbers, 'destroying' them. The winner is the first to have destroyed their opponent's defences.

☆ Play two games.

Game 1

Player 1			Player 2	
-3	-8		-33	23
-22	-31		91	0
30	7		17	-28
-58	-27		-10	80
18	0		-50	-25
-12	10		-2	-9

Game 2

Player 1			Player 2	
-1	17		-39	38
-19	-11		18	-2
33	-17		-25	-41
-49	-53		-16	-18
-8	9		-54	-25
-27	32		-9	4

NOW TRY THIS!

- ## Now write ten pairs of positive and negative numbers with a difference of 17.

Teachers' note Suggest that the child with the shortest first name goes first in game 1 and then swap for game 2 to make it fairer. Give the children a negative number line to check the differences and encourage them to use zero as a stopover when finding the difference between 20 a positive and negative number.

A Lesson for Every Day
Maths
10-11 Years
© A&C Black

Snowflakes

Each line of decimals forms a sequence.

- **Continue the sequences and fill in the missing decimals.**

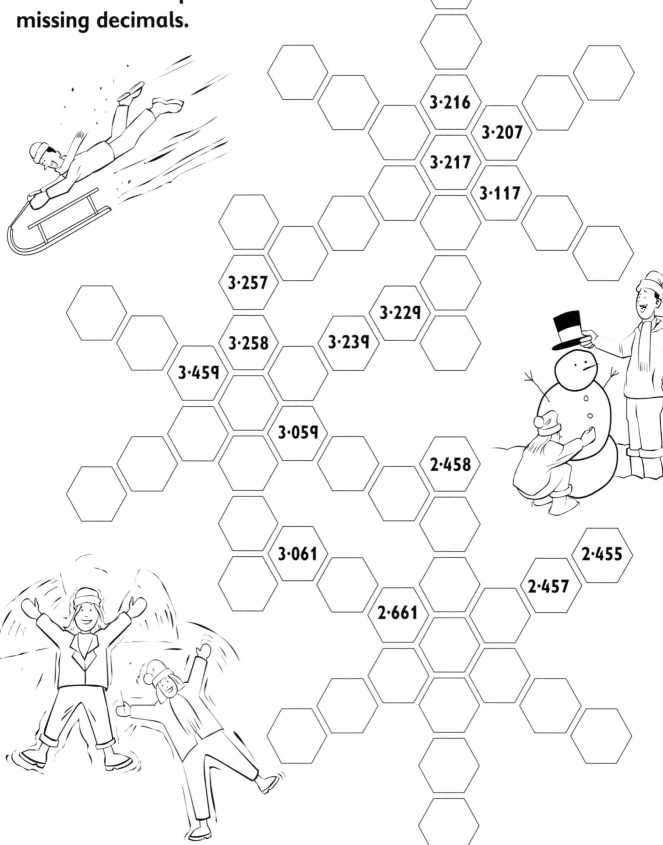

3·216

3·207

3·217

3·117

3·257

3·229

3·258   3·239

3·459

3·059

2·458

3·061

2·455

2·457

2·661

Teachers' note Encourage the children to describe each sequence using the words tenths, hundredths or thousandths, for example, this sequence is increasing in steps of 2 tenths each time, or this goes up in steps of one thousandth. As an extension activity, ask the children to find six pairs of numbers in the snowflakes that have a difference of 1.

A Lesson for Every Day
Maths
10–11 Years
© A&C Black

Totals and products

Two integers have a total of (20). What is their product?

1. Find all the possible products, not including zero.

| 1 | × | 19 | = | 19 |

| | × | | = | |

| | × | | = | |

| | × | | = | |

| | × | | = | |

| | × | | = | |

| | × | | = | |

| | × | | = | |

| | × | | = | |

| | × | | = | |

Two integers have a total of (74). One number is a single-digit integer and the other is a two-digit integer.

2. Find all the possible products.

| | × | | = | |

| | × | | = | |

| | × | | = | |

| | × | | = | |

| | × | | = | |

| | × | | = | |

| | × | | = | |

| | × | | = | |

| | × | | = | |

| | × | | = | |

NOW TRY THIS!

- **To check your answers, use a calculator but do _not_ use the multiplication key. Use the inverse operation instead.**

Teachers' note Encourage the children to use appropriate mental methods, for example using partitioning and making jottings. Ensure the children are aware that they can use zero as the single-digit integer in the second activity. Discuss how the division key on the calculator should be used to check their products. The numbers in the circles could be altered to provide further variety.

A Lesson for Every Day
Maths
10-11 Years
© A&C Black

Prediction patterns

The shapes in each repeating pattern are numbered.

- Predict the shape and colour of other numbers in the pattern.
- Explain to a partner how you know.

1   ⋯

The 35th shape will be a ___ white triangle ___.

2     ⋯

The 40th shape will be a _____.

3   ⋯

The 27th shape will be a _____.

4   ⋯

The 29th shape will be a _____.

5   ⋯

The 59th shape will be a _____.

NOW TRY THIS!

- **Draw a repeating pattern of shapes around these numbers.**

1   2   3   4   5   6   7   8   9   10

- **Predict the colour and shape of the 100th shape in your sequence.**

The 100th shape will be a _____

Teachers' note Ensure the children realise that the two colours used in the sequences are white and grey. Encourage the children to describe their reasoning and to explain how they tackled each pattern.

A Lesson for Every Day
Maths
10–11 Years
© A&C Black

Problems, problems

(125 ÷ 5) × 6	(12·5 ÷ 5) + 6
(125 − 26) ÷ 9	(12·50 + 26) × 9
18·9 ÷ (3 × 2)	(189 × 3) ÷ 2
(1·89 + 3·17) × 7	1·89 + (3·17 × 7)
26 − 34 + 12	(26 + 34) ÷ 12
(2·6 + 3·4) × 9	(0·26 + 3·4) × 9
(450 ÷ 9) × 8	(450 × 9) ÷ 8
8000 − (450 × 9)	800 + (450 ÷ 9)

☆ Colour any three of the calculations in the grid above.

☆ Write two **different** word problems to match each of your chosen calculations.

☆ Write each word problem on one of the cards below.

☆ Cut out the cards and give them to a partner to solve.

Teachers' note Encourage the children to use a variety of words and contexts in their problems. When the children swap cards, they should try to identify the calculation and the two related cards, and then solve the problem. Stress the importance of giving the correct unit in the answer and of checking that the solution makes sense in the context of the problem.

A Lesson for Every Day
Maths
10–11 Years
© A&C Black

Pesky pets!

Matty's pet mice have escaped and have nibbled his homework!

• **Use a calculator to find the missing digits.**

1 $16 \times \boxed{7} = 112$

2 $\boxed{} \times 14 = 126$

3 $\boxed{}92 \div 8 = 61 \cdot 5$

4 $66 - \boxed{}\boxed{} = 29$

5 $\boxed{}\boxed{} + 37 = 51$

6 $\boxed{}\boxed{} \times \boxed{} = 65$

7 $180 \div \boxed{} \cdot \boxed{} = 40$

8 $17 \cdot 4 \times \boxed{} \cdot \boxed{} = 163 \cdot 56$

9 $568 \cdot 1 \div \boxed{}\boxed{} = 24 \cdot 7$

10 $35 \cdot 6 + 8\boxed{} \cdot 5 = 121 \cdot 1$

11 $593 - 20\boxed{} = 3\boxed{}1$

12 $64 \cdot \boxed{} + \boxed{}3 \cdot 2 = 158$

NOW TRY THIS!

The <u>same</u> number is missing from each box.

• **Write the <u>same</u> missing number in each box.**

$$\boxed{} \times \boxed{} \times \boxed{} = 6859$$

Teachers' note Provide the children with calculators for this activity. Ask the children to describe what they did to solve each problem. As a further extension, they can create their own missing number problems for a partner to solve.

A Lesson for Every Day
Maths
10–11 Years
© A&C Black

Strategy sorting

- **Cut out the cards and sort them with a partner.**
- **Decide which calculations you would work out:**

* entirely in your head
* using jottings
* using a written method
* using a calculator
* using a combination of these strategies.

£50 increased by 100%	£24 decreased by 5%
£274 increased by 32%	£50 decreased by 10%
£160 increased by 2%	£240 decreased by 11%
£13.50 increased by 6%	£8 decreased by 2%
£33 increased by 40%	£64 decreased by 50%
£72 increased by 7%	£79 decreased by 3%
£659 increased by 37%	£150 decreased by 66·6%
£90 increased by 99%	£68 decreased by 20%
£88 increased by 25%	£260 decreased by 75%

Teachers' note Encourage the children to work with their partner to solve each problem, recording the answer and strategy on the reverse of the card and then grouping the cards according to the approach they used. Where children are over-using a calculator, ask them to write out the order of keys that they press each time, as a record of their strategy.

A Lesson for Every Day
Maths
10–11 Years
© A&C Black

33

Decimal puzzle: 1

- Cut out the small hexagons and arrange them onto the large hexagons to show each decimal on the large hexagon rounded to the nearest whole number.

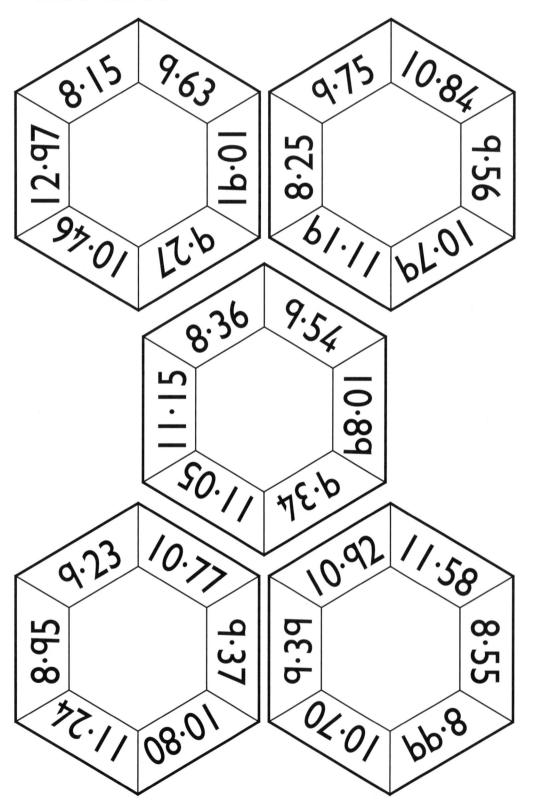

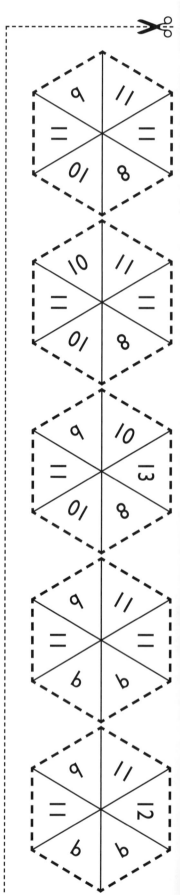

Teachers' note Ensure the children understand that there is only one correct position that each small hexagon can be placed where all the decimals are correctly rounded to the nearest whole number. Remind them that the digit 5 is rounded up, for example 4·5 is rounded to 5 and 3·53 is rounded to 4.

A Lesson for Every Day
Maths
10–11 Years
© A&C Black

Decimal puzzle: 2

- **Cut out the small hexagons and arrange them onto the large hexagons to show each decimal on the large hexagon rounded to the nearest tenth.**

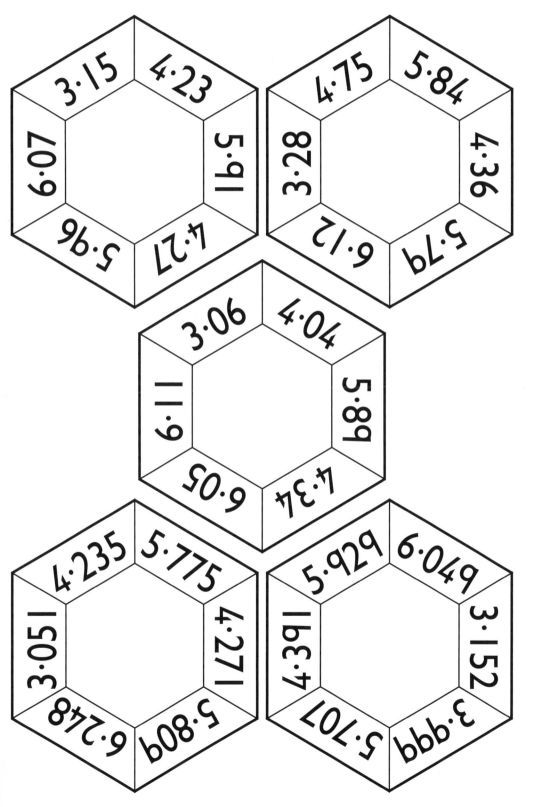

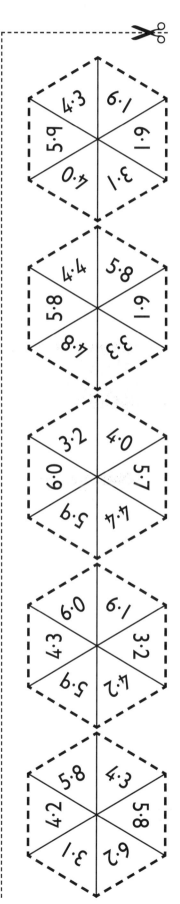

Teachers' note Ensure the children understand that there is only one correct position that each small hexagon can be placed where all the decimals are correctly rounded to the nearest tenth. Remind them that the digit 5 is rounded up, for example 4·35 is rounded to 4·4 and 2·953 is rounded to 3·0.

A Lesson for Every Day
Maths
10–11 Years
© A&C Black

Decimal hops

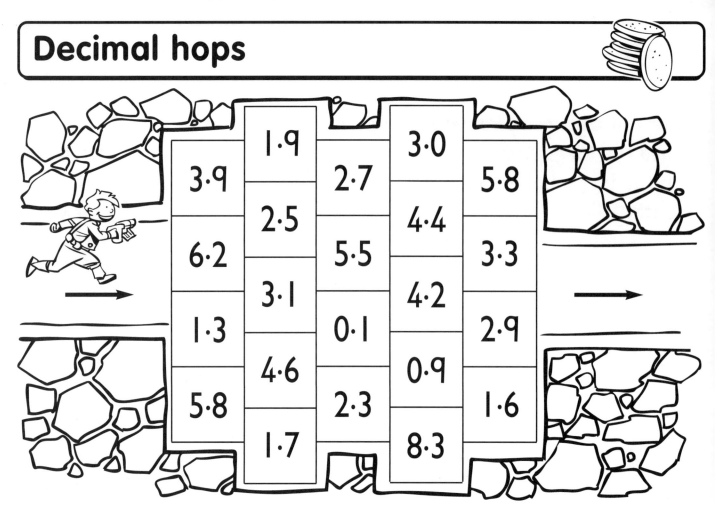

To find a trail, move from square to square and cross from one side of the grid to the other. The squares must be touching.

- **Write some trails to match these totals.**

(11·9)	= 6·2 + 3·1 + 0·1 + 0·9 + 1·6 _____
(13·5)	_____
(19·7)	_____
(18·6)	_____
(16·2)	_____
(20·2)	_____

NOW TRY THIS!

- **What is the smallest total you can find?**

_____

Teachers' note Demonstrate appropriate strategies for adding and subtracting decimals mentally, such as adding a whole number and adjusting, or partitioning. The decimals could be altered to provide differentiation.

A Lesson for Every Day
Maths
10–11 Years
© A&C Black

Annette's baguettes

Annette has a baguette stall. Here is her price list.

Cheese and tomato	£2.29
Bacon and brie	£3.29
Ham salad	£2.79
Chicken tikka	£3.09
Egg mayonnaise	£2.49
Roast lamb	£3.39
Tuna mayo	£2.89
BLT	£3.49

- **Work out how much change to give each customer.**

1.  I'd like a Bacon and brie and a Tuna mayo. £10

£3·82 change

2. I'd like a Ham salad and a Chicken tikka. £20

☐ change

3.  I'd like a Roast lamb, a Cheese and tomato £20 and a BLT.

☐ change

4.  I'd like a Tuna mayo and an Egg mayonnaise.

☐ change

5.  I'd like a Roast lamb, a Bacon and brie, a BLT and a Tuna mayo. £10 £5

☐ change

6.  I'd like a Tuna mayo, a Chicken tikka and a Ham salad. £10

☐ change

NOW TRY THIS!

Four different baguettes were bought.
- **Work out three possible total costs of these.**

Teachers' note The children could use any appropriate mental or written methods to solve these problems. This activity could be developed further by displaying a baguette list on the classroom wall and asking the children to work in groups to choose their lunch and find how much each set of baguettes would cost.

Digit discoveries

- **What is special about the digits of the decimals in these subtraction questions?** _____

- **Use written methods to answer the questions.**

  1. 54·321 – 9·876 = _____

  2. 65·432 – 10·987 = _____

  3. 76·543 – 21·098 = _____

  4. 87·654 – 32·109 = _____

  5. 98·765 – 43·21 = _____

- **What do you notice about the answers?**

  _____

  _____

  _____

  _____

Show your method here.

NOW TRY THIS!

- **Continue this pattern and answer the questions. What do you notice this time?**

  (a) 32·109 – 9·876 = _____

  (b) 43·21 – 10·987 = _____

  (c) 54·321 – 21·098 = _____

  (d) 65·432 – 32·109 = _____

  (e) 76·543 – 43·21 = _____

  (f) _____ – _____ = _____

  (g) _____ – _____ = _____

- **Explore similar patterns in this way.**

Show your method here.

Teachers' note This activity encourages the children to use written methods to subtract decimals, including those with different numbers of digits.

A Lesson for Every Day
Maths
10–11 Years
© A&C Black

Walter Wall carpets

Walter Wall has a carpet shop. He buys lengths of carpet and pays a price per metre of length.

1. Find the cost of each length of carpet using written methods of multiplication.

(a) Length: 25 m
Price per m: £17

(b) Length: 37 m
Price per m: £12

(c) Length: 19 m
Price per m: £28

(d) Length: 24 m
Price per m: £36

(e) Length: 52 m
Price per m: £24

(f) Length: 76 m
Price per m: £19

2. Which length of carpet is the most expensive? _____

NOW TRY THIS!

- **If the standard width of a carpet is 4 metres, find the** area **of each carpet above.**
- **What is the price of each carpet per square metre of area?**

Record on a separate piece of paper.

Talk to a partner about how you can find out.

Teachers' note Discuss and demonstrate appropriate written methods for answering these questions, such as using short or long multiplication, or using the grid method. 'TU × TU: expanded' and 'TU × TU: short' could be used as a basis for the multiplication of two-digit numbers. Provide a calculator for the last part of the extension activity.

A Lesson for Every Day
Maths
10–11 Years
© A&C Black

TU x TU: expanded

- **Use these grids to help you multiply pairs of two-digit numbers together.**

estimate _____

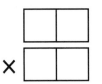

$$\begin{array}{c|c|c|c}\hline & & 0 & 0 \\\hline\end{array}\quad (\underline{}0 \times \underline{}0)$$

$$\begin{array}{c|c|c|c}\hline & & & 0 \\\hline\end{array}\quad (\underline{} \times \underline{}0)$$

$$\begin{array}{c|c|c|c}\hline & & & 0 \\\hline\end{array}\quad (\underline{}0 \times \underline{})$$

$$\quad (\underline{} \times \underline{})$$

estimate _____

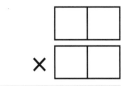

$$\begin{array}{c|c|c|c}\hline & & 0 & 0 \\\hline\end{array}\quad (\underline{}0 \times \underline{}0)$$

$$\begin{array}{c|c|c|c}\hline & & & 0 \\\hline\end{array}\quad (\underline{} \times \underline{}0)$$

$$\begin{array}{c|c|c|c}\hline & & & 0 \\\hline\end{array}\quad (\underline{}0 \times \underline{})$$

$$\quad (\underline{} \times \underline{})$$

estimate _____

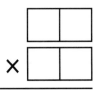

$$\begin{array}{c|c|c|c}\hline & & 0 & 0 \\\hline\end{array}\quad (\underline{}0 \times \underline{}0)$$

$$\begin{array}{c|c|c|c}\hline & & & 0 \\\hline\end{array}\quad (\underline{} \times \underline{}0)$$

$$\begin{array}{c|c|c|c}\hline & & & 0 \\\hline\end{array}\quad (\underline{}0 \times \underline{})$$

$$\quad (\underline{} \times \underline{})$$

estimate _____

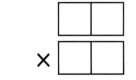

$$\begin{array}{c|c|c|c}\hline & & 0 & 0 \\\hline\end{array}\quad (\underline{}0 \times \underline{}0)$$

$$\begin{array}{c|c|c|c}\hline & & & 0 \\\hline\end{array}\quad (\underline{} \times \underline{}0)$$

$$\begin{array}{c|c|c|c}\hline & & & 0 \\\hline\end{array}\quad (\underline{}0 \times \underline{})$$

$$\quad (\underline{} \times \underline{})$$

Teachers' note This sheet can be given to the children to help them solve questions written on the board. Alternatively, appropriate two-digit × two-digit questions can be filled in before the sheet is given to the children. See the notes on the activity on page 7 for how to complete these diagrams.

A Lesson for Every Day
Maths
10–11 Years
© A&C Black

TU x TU: short

- **Use these grids to help you multiply pairs of two-digit numbers together.**

---

estimate _____

$\times$

0   (___ ___ × ___0)

(___ ___ × ___)

---

estimate _____

$\times$

0   (___ ___ × ___0)

(___ ___ × ___)

---

estimate _____

$\times$

0   (___ ___ × ___0)

(___ ___ × ___)

---

estimate _____

$\times$

0   (___ ___ × ___0)

(___ ___ × ___)

---

estimate _____

$\times$

0   (___ ___ × ___0)

(___ ___ × ___)

---

estimate _____

$\times$

0   (___ ___ × ___0)

(___ ___ × ___)

Teachers' note This sheet can be given to the children to help them solve questions written on the board. Alternatively, appropriate two-digit × two-digit questions can be filled in before the sheet is given to the children. See the notes on the activity on page 7 for how to complete these diagrams.

A Lesson for Every Day
Maths
10–11 Years
© A&C Black

Crazy creepy crawlies

- Use 10 small cubes or counters to represent 10 creepy crawlies. Arrange the creepy crawlies so that there are:

  | 7 | in hoop **A**, | 3 | in hoop **B** and | 6 | in hoop **C**.

Have you noticed that the total of these three numbers is <u>not</u> 10 – it is 16! Talk to a partner about why this is.

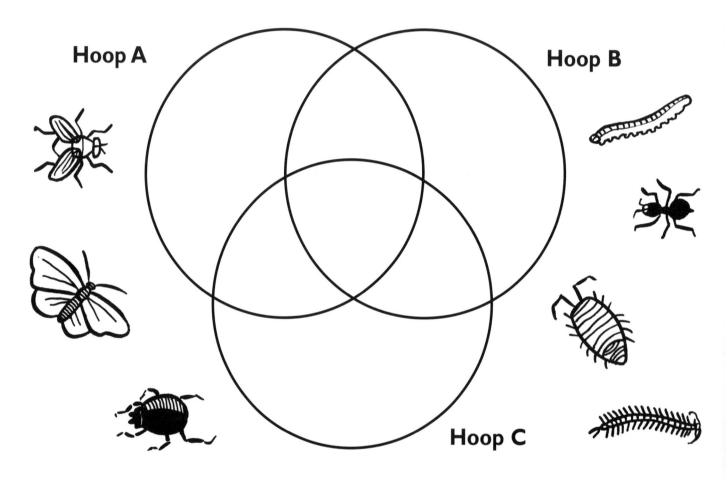

Hoop A

Hoop B

Hoop C

- Investigate other ways of arranging 10 creepy crawlies in the hoops, and write how many are in each hoop.

NOW TRY THIS!

- How could you show your findings in a table?
- Can you find the highest and lowest possible totals of the three numbers in the hoops?
- Are any totals in between impossible to make?

Teachers' note Ensure the children understand that they should always have ten creepy crawlies, but that the totals of the three hoop numbers can vary according to where the creepy crawlies are placed in the hoops. See the notes on the activity on page 8 for more information. Encourage the children to explain and represent their findings using numbers, diagrams, words or symbols.

A Lesson for Every Day
Maths
10-11 Years
© A&C Black

Calculator errors

Each person has made a calculator error.

- **What might he or she have done wrong?**
- **Show how _you_ would have tackled the calculations.**

---

1 George used a calculator to work out 15% of £40.
He got a wrong answer of £600.

2 Suzie used a calculator to work out $\frac{3}{8}$ of 216 ml.
She got a wrong answer of 576 ml.

3 Martina used a calculator to work out (12% of 36 kg) + 4 kg.
She got a wrong answer of 7 kg.

4 Asif used a calculator to work out 7 × (285 + 348).
He got a wrong answer of 2343.

NOW TRY THIS!

- **Talk to a partner about which question you found the hardest.**

Teachers' note Provide the children with calculators for this activity. It is important that the children are given the opportunity to explain how they would have worked out each answer, and to suggest why they think each person might have made an error.

A Lesson for Every Day
Maths
10–11 Years
© A&C Black

What do you notice?

- **Solve each problem and show the calculation that you used.**

Work with a partner.

---

1 Three cups of tea and two biscuits together cost £2.17.

One cup of tea costs 45p.

What is the price of a biscuit?

2 The sum of these number cards is 34.

If the cards marked A show the number 8, what number is on both of the B cards?

---

3 Three identical erasers are spaced equally along the length of a 30 cm ruler.

gap   gap

Each eraser is 6 cm in length. How long is each gap?

4 The total mass of three apples and two lemons is 545 g.

If each apple weighs 125 g, what is the mass of one lemon?

- **Now talk to your partner about what you notice about these problems.**

NOW TRY THIS!

- **Make up another problem that is similar to the ones above. Show the calculations you would use to answer your problem.**

Teachers' note The numbers and prices can be altered to provide differentiation. Provide the children with calculators for this activity. Encourage the children to describe their strategy and/or calculation for working out each answer, including saying whether they used mental methods, written methods, or a calculator.

A Lesson for Every Day
Maths
10–11 Years
© A&C Black

Weighty questions

- **This table shows the weight of some animals.**

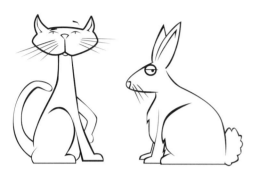

kilograms	animals
less than 2	budgie
2 ≤ **k** < 4	cat
4 ≤ **k** < 6	hare
6 ≤ **k** < 8	raccoon
8 ≤ **k** < 10	dog

The numbers below show the weights of different animals.

- **Put them in order of size, smallest first.**

1

3·55	2·421
2·421	2·425
2·425	
3·4	
3	
2·5	
3·099	

2

4·074	
3·725	
2·8	
4·462	
3·98	
3·0	
2·789	

3

7·695	
7·975	
7·765	
7·9	
7·0	
7·567	
7·65	

4

8·531	
8·5	
8·135	
8·51	
8·315	
8·3	
8·513	

NOW TRY THIS!

- **On paper, sort all the decimals into the five groups shown in the table.**

Teachers' note At the start of the lesson discuss the 'less than' and 'less than or equal to' signs and the notation 2 ≤ k < 4 where k stands for the number of kilograms. Explain that this means numbers that lie between 2 and 4, including the number 2 itself.

A Lesson for Every Day
Maths
10–11 Years
© A&C Black

Coconut shy

- ## Write the correct decimals on the coconuts.

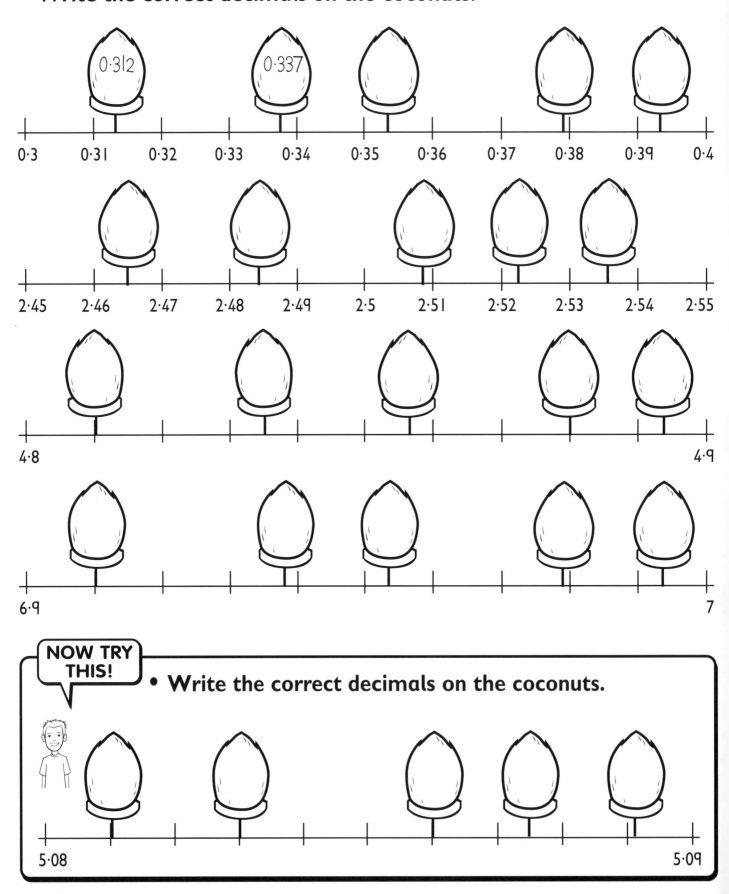

0·312   0·337

| 0·3 | 0·31 | 0·32 | 0·33 | 0·34 | 0·35 | 0·36 | 0·37 | 0·38 | 0·39 | 0·4 |

| 2·45 | 2·46 | 2·47 | 2·48 | 2·49 | 2·5 | 2·51 | 2·52 | 2·53 | 2·54 | 2·55 |

4·8   4·9

6·9   7

NOW TRY THIS!

- ## Write the correct decimals on the coconuts.

5·08   5·09

Teachers' note Some children will find it easier to write all the decimals of the marked points under the line for the third, fourth and fifth number lines. Point out that the decimals marked on the line in the extension activity are in hundredths, rather than tenths.

A Lesson for Every Day
Maths
10–11 Years
© A&C Black

46

Decimal puzzle: 3

- **Cut out the small hexagons and arrange them onto the large hexagons to show each decimal on the large hexagon rounded to the nearest hundredth.**

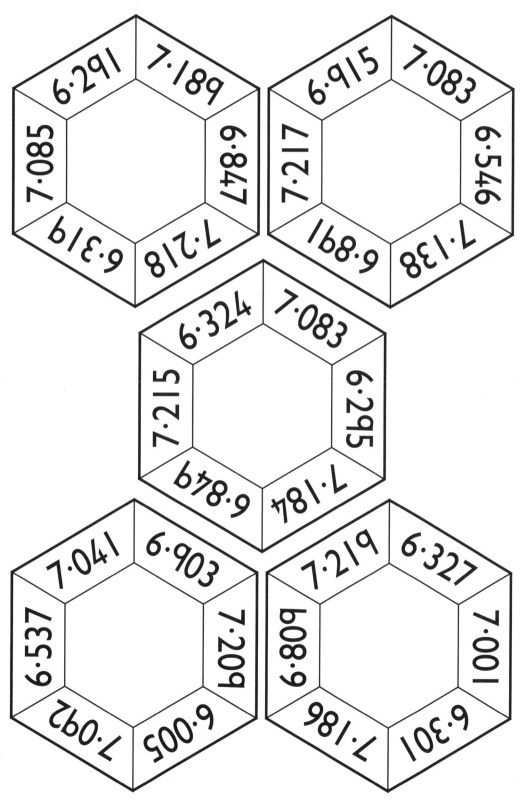

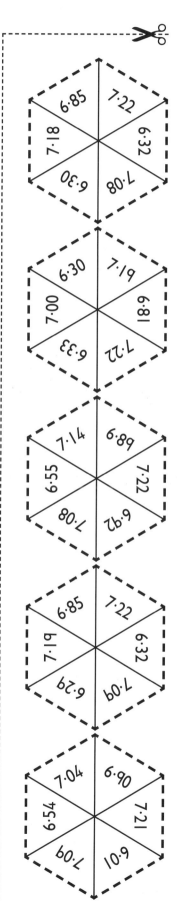

Teachers' note Ensure the children understand that there is only one correct position that each small hexagon can be placed where all the decimals are correctly rounded to the nearest hundredth. Remind them that the digit 5 is rounded up, for example 4·385 is rounded to 4·39 and 2·395 is rounded to 2·40 (to the nearest hundredth).

A Lesson for Every Day
Maths
10–11 Years
© A&C Black

Dice nets

- **Cut out and make each dice to use with the 'Going mental' games.**

Dice 1

4·5

5·6 3·6 4·2

8·1

2·8

Dice 2

3·7

5·2

9·5 6·3 9·2

7·8

Dice 3

4

8 9 5 9

7

Teachers' note Use these dice in conjunction with 'Going mental: 1 and 2'. (This sheet could be photo-copied onto A3 and stuck onto thin card if preferred.) Ask the children to make a note of which is dice 1, dice 2 and dice 3 before cutting them out.

A Lesson for Every Day
Maths
10–11 Years
© A&C Black

Going mental: 1

• **Play these games with a partner.**

Game 1 Addition and subtraction

☆ Take turns to roll both dice.

☆ Choose whether to find the <u>sum</u> or the <u>difference</u> of the two numbers using mental methods to find the answer.

☆ Your partner should check your answer using a calculator.

☆ If it is correct and appears on the sheet, cover the answer with a counter in your colour.

☆ The winner is the first player with four counters on the sheet.

You need dice 1 and 2 from the 'Dice nets' sheet and small counters in two colours.

2·2	0·3	1·8	11·8	11·4	3·5	0·5
0·4	12·3	2·9	0·1	12	0·7	15·9
7·1	5	5·2	8·2	10·6	3·3	0·9
15·1	7·3	0·3	10·8	14	6·5	17·6
5·3	8·8	1·6	5·9	14·4	7·9	1·6
2·7	11	2·1	8·5	9·4	0·1	8

Game 2 Addition and rounding

☆ Each player writes the numbers 10 to 25 on a piece of paper.

☆ Take turns to roll the three dice and mentally find the <u>sum</u> of the three numbers.

☆ Your partner should check your answer using a calculator.

☆ Round the answer to the nearest whole number.

☆ If the number is on your list, cross it off.

☆ The winner is the first player to cross off all their numbers or to have the most crossed off after 20 minutes.

You need dice 1, 2 and 3 from the 'Dice nets' sheet.

Teachers' note This activity helps children to practise adding and subtracting U.t numbers. The second game also involves rounding decimals to the nearest whole number.

A Lesson for Every Day
Maths
10-11 Years
© A&C Black

Going mental: 2

- **Play these games with a partner.**

Game 1 Multiplication

☆ One of you is Player 1 and the other Player 2.

☆ Roll both dice. Both players should use mental methods to find the product of the two numbers.

☆ If you both agree on the answer, look for it in the grids below and cross it off.

☆ You can only cross off one number at a time in each grid.

☆ The first player to cross off eight numbers wins the game.

You need dice 1 and dice 3 from the 'Dice nets' sheet for both games.

Player 1

33·6	22·5	18
28	16·8	27
22·4	31·5	40·5
21·6	32·4	33·6
29·4	25·2	40·5
22·4	11·2	48·6

Player 2

37·8	21	50·4
36	28·8	19·6
39·2	44·8	14
14·4	25·2	18
56·7	32·4	64·8
16·8	25·2	72·9

Game 2 Division

☆ Roll both dice.

☆ **If the shapes on each dice match**, both players should use mental methods to divide the decimal by the whole number.

☆ **If the shapes do not match**, roll again.

☆ As for game 1, cross off the answer in the grids.

Player 1

0·75	0·84
0·7	1·4
1·12	0·8
0·6	0·7
1·35	0·4

Player 2

0·7	0·56
0·4	0·9
1·62	0·4
0·72	0·6
0·5	0·35

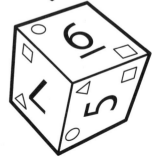

Teachers' note Encourage the children to work mentally with jotting to find answers to the multiplications and divisions. Children could use dice 2 and dice 3 for alternative practice in multiplying and dividing decimals with one place by whole numbers.

A Lesson for Every Day
Maths
10–11 Years
© A&C Black

On the ball

Here are the diameters and masses
of different types of sports ball.

Ball type	Diameter	Mass
football	22·65 cm	464·1 g
snooker	5·25 cm	120·5 g
table tennis	3·9 cm	2·68 g
cricket	7·13 cm	155·9 g
volleyball	21·4 cm	271·3 g
tennis	6·35 cm	58·9 g
squash	4·04 cm	24·7 g
hockey	7·32 cm	158 g

- **Answer these questions using an
  appropriate written method.**

Show your method on
a separate piece of paper.

1. How much **larger** is the diameter of a volleyball than:

   (a) a cricket ball? _____ cm   **(b)** a table tennis ball? _____ cm

   (c) a squash ball? _____ cm   **(d)** a snooker ball? _____ cm

   (e) a tennis ball? _____ cm   **(f)** a hockey ball? _____ cm

2. How much **lighter** is a table tennis ball than:

   (a) a volleyball? _____ g   **(b)** a football? _____ g

   (c) a squash ball? _____ g   **(d)** a snooker ball? _____ g

   (e) a cricket ball? _____ g   **(f)** a tennis ball? _____ g

NOW TRY THIS!

Imagine that all of the balls are placed in a bag.
- **If the total mass of the balls and the bag is 1·3 kg,
  what is the mass of the bag? _____ g**

Teachers' note The children should use written methods to solve these problems. Encourage them to
think carefully about how to set out the digits if using standard column methods.

A Lesson for Every Day
Maths
10–11 Years
© A&C Black

9 to 1 challenge

☆ The digits 9 to 1, in order, can be used to make different calculations.

Example: | 987 – 65·4 + 3·21 | | 9 + 876·54 – 32·1 |

6 2 5
9 4 1 3
7   8

☆ Each calculation has three numbers. They can be whole numbers or decimals. Each calculation has an addition sign and a subtraction sign.

☆ Write some calculations like these and work out the answers using written methods.

NOW TRY THIS!

Two of the numbers are decimals and the answer is a whole number.
- **Find three calculations that match this description.**

Teachers' note If the children are to use column methods of addition and subtraction, remind them of the importance of lining up the digits correctly. For the extension activity, provide the children with scrap paper – they could then record their three calculations on the back of this sheet.

A Lesson for Every Day
Maths
10–11 Years
© A&C Black

The mummy's riddle

• ## What is the answer to the mummy's riddle?

Use written methods.

A calculation, that is me,
No ordinary one, as soon you'll see.
Look at these digits, they are mine:
2 and **4, 6, 8** and **9**.
They really look so very fine
On either side of a multiplication sign.
My integers, of course, are on the number line:
My first is less than 109, my second more than 209.
Solutions to this problem do abound
But what's the largest answer to be found?

Workings

98 × 642 =

NOW TRY THIS!

Lines 7 and 8 of the riddle are changed:

My decimals, of course, are on the number line:
My first is less than 10, my second less than 9.

• ## On a separate piece of paper, find the largest answer.

Teachers' note Discuss and demonstrate appropriate written methods for answering these questions. Encourage the children to make estimates before calculating. The children will need extra paper for the extension activity and, possibly, for the main activity.

A Lesson for Every Day
Maths
10–11 Years
© A&C Black

Tile teaser

- **Cut out the number tiles.**
- **Arrange the numbers on this grid so that the total of each row, column and diagonal is an even number.**

- **Write what you notice about the number of odd and even numbers in each row and column.**

_____

_____

- **What do you notice about the diagonals?**

_____

_____

1	2	3	4	5	6	7	8
9	10	11	12	13	14	15	16

Teachers' note As an extension, ask the children to find different solutions and to explain what they notice. As a further extension, the children could be encouraged to swap odd numbers (or even numbers) around to create new solutions. This could lead on to the creation of a magic square, where each row, column and diagonal have the same total.

A Lesson for Every Day
Maths
10-11 Years
© A&C Black

Sequence squares

- **Count the number of small squares in each of the shapes in a row and write them as a sequence.**
- **Write the next three numbers in each sequence.**

One has been started for you.

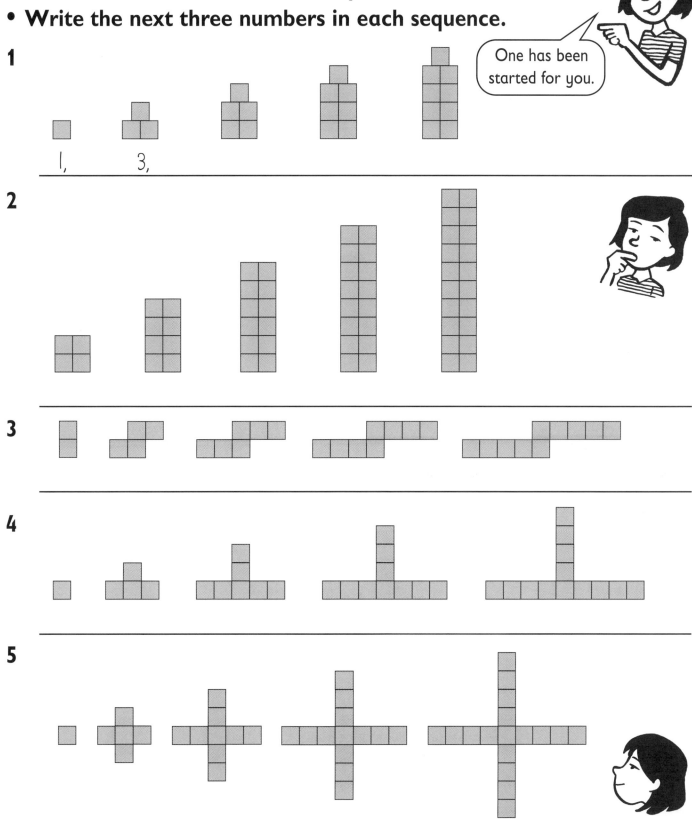

1

1,   3,

2

3

4

5

Teachers' note As the children write the rules for each sequence, they could be encouraged to think about and predict other terms in the sequence, for example, the tenth term or the hundredth term. This encourages them to think more about the relationship with the number and its position, rather than merely looking at the term-to-term relationship.

A Lesson for Every Day
Maths
10-11 Years
© A&C Black

Is it possible?

- **Work with a partner to see whether you think each question is possible.**
- **Justify your answers and give examples.**

1

Is it possible to arrange the digits 7, 5 and 8 to make a three-digit number that is **not divisible** by 9?

2

Is it possible to arrange the digits 1, 0 and 9 to make a three-digit number that is **divisible** by 5?

3

Is it possible to arrange the digits 4, 8 and 6 to make a three-digit number that is **not divisible** by 6?

4

Is it possible to arrange the digits 1, 7 and 9 to make a three-digit number that is **divisible** by 8?

5

Is it possible to arrange the digits 4, 5 and 9 to make a three-digit number that is **divisible** by 4?

Teachers' note Encourage the children to explain their reasoning and to justify their views. Rather than just trying all possibilities, ask them to explain what is special about the multiples and the sums or natures of the digits given.

A Lesson for Every Day
Maths
10–11 Years
© A&C Black

Tables testing cards

- **Cut out Tests A, B and C and write the answers.**
- **Cut out strips A, B and C to check whether your answers are correct.**

Test A	Test B	Test C	A	B	C
0·3 × 5 = _____	9 × 0·9 = _____	0·4 × 7 = _____	1·5	8·1	2·8
6 × 0·4 = _____	0·5 × 7 = _____	6 × 0·6 = _____	2·4	3·5	3·6
0·9 × 2 = _____	8 × 0·8 = _____	6 × 0·4 = _____	1·8	6·4	2·4
7 × 0·3 = _____	0·6 × 10 = _____	8 × 0·5 = _____	2·1	6	4
0·5 × 5 = _____	8 × 0·2 = _____	0·7 × 7 = _____	2·5	1·6	4·9
6 × 0·9 = _____	0·2 × 2 = _____	9 × 0·8 = _____	5·4	0·4	7·2
0·4 × 3 = _____	6 × 0·7 = _____	0·9 × 5 = _____	1·2	4·2	4·5
3 × 0·2 = _____	0·9 × 4 = _____	7 × 0·8 = _____	0·6	3·6	5·6
0·5 × 4 = _____	10 × 0·3 = _____	8 × 0·6 = _____	2	3	4·8
0·6 × 10 = _____	0·5 × 2 = _____	0·9 × 7 = _____	6	1	6·3
4 × 0·4 = _____	3 × 0·9 = _____	9 × 0·9 = _____	1·6	2·7	8·1
0·8 × 3 = _____	0·7 × 2 = _____	7 × 0·5 = _____	2·4	1·4	3·5
5 × 0·6 = _____	6 × 0·6 = _____	0·8 × 8 = _____	3	3·6	6·4
0·4 × 2 = _____	0 × 0·6 = _____	6 × 0·4 = _____	0·8	0	2·4
3 × 0·6 = _____	0·5 × 8 = _____	0·3 × 7 = _____	1·8	4	2·1
0·4 × 10 = _____	7 × 0·7 = _____	9 × 0·6 = _____	4·0	4·9	5·4
3 × 0·3 = _____	0·9 × 8 = _____	0·7 × 6 = _____	0·9	7·2	4·2
0·8 × 4 = _____	5 × 0·9 = _____	4 × 0·9 = _____	3·2	4·5	3·6
6 × 0·2 = _____	0·8 × 7 = _____	0·8 × 6 = _____	1·2	5·6	4·8
0·7 × 4 = _____	10 × 0·8 = _____	3 × 0·4 = _____	2·8	8	1·2

Teachers' note These cards can be cut out and used as testing cards for decimal facts related to the tables up to 10 × 10. Encourage the children to note each time they try a test which questions and answers they got wrong or could not work out and to learn them.

A Lesson for Every Day
Maths
10–11 Years
© A&C Black

Rounding riddles

- **Tick the box to show whether each statement is true or false.**

1. 3060 + 1799 is more than 3000 + 1800   ☐ True ☐ False

2. 385 × 19 is less than 400 × 20   ☐ True ☐ False

3. 601 ÷ 28 is more than 600 ÷ 30   ☐ True ☐ False

4. 5618 – 3695 is more than 5600 – 3700   ☐ True ☐ False

5. 3592 + 4165 is less than 3600 + 4200   ☐ True ☐ False

6. 291 × 28 is more than 300 × 30   ☐ True ☐ False

7. 807 ÷ 19 is less than 800 ÷ 20   ☐ True ☐ False

8. 6214 – 4887 is more than 6200 – 4900   ☐ True ☐ False

9. 7389 + 5062 is more than 7400 + 5100   ☐ True ☐ False

10. 753 × 39 is less than 800 × 40   ☐ True ☐ False

11. 813 ÷ 48 is less than 800 ÷ 50   ☐ True ☐ False

12. 9431 + 5215 is more than 9400 + 5200   ☐ True ☐ False

NOW TRY THIS!

- **Make up your own rounding riddles for a partner to solve.**

58

Teachers' note This activity encourages the children to think in more detail about their approximations, rather than just rounding. Encourage them to consider the effect that rounding both numbers to the nearest 10 has in a division such as 155 ÷ 16, where it might be more appropriate not to round the second number, for example 160 ÷ 20 = 8 but 160 ÷ 16 = 10 is a better estimate.

A Lesson for Every Day
Maths
10–11 Years
© A&C Black

Hidden letters

- In each grid, shade the numbers that are divisible by the number on the robot's head.

2

88	104	978
426	387	77
92	606	212
931	243	80
718	300	510

10

80	25	560
70	805	970
150	125	210
330	804	900
750	480	840

5

15	290	720
80	52	700
615	525	445
800	507	528
705	807	56

3

333	786	216
183	260	418
912	564	108
366	943	625
783	372	123

4

480	128	756
660	438	324
164	388	962
536	514	776
892	266	392

6

462	248	624
528	842	750
234	312	378
924	496	984
468	226	786

8

584	312	960
480	436	870
248	688	352
760	214	906
512	936	272

9

720	549	477
243	361	819
729	612	784
333	496	171
675	838	531

25

525	150	375
275	460	425
800	515	750
625	870	100
900	350	625

- **Write the word hidden in the grids.** _____

Teachers' note As an extension activity, ask the children to write instructions for how to work out which numbers are divisible by each of the numbers 2, 3, 4, 5, 6, 8, 9, 10 and 25. See page 9 for further information.

A Lesson for Every Day
Maths
10-11 Years
© A&C Black

Inverses in verses

- **Use inverses to check whether each statement is true or false. Write what you will do to check and use a calculator.**

1. Eighty-five times twenty-four, The answer's written on this door. **2040**

$2040 \div 24 = 85$
True

2. Three hundred and seventy-eight, When divided by six, Is shown upon this plate. **63**

3. One thousand and twenty-three, Plus four hundred and seventy, You'll find the answer here to see: **1503**

4. Take six hundred and forty-nine, From ten thousand, Now look at the sign: **351**

5. The product of seventy-eight and two Is written here upon this shoe. **156**

6. I have five thousand, two hundred and one, I divide it by seven, now what have I done? Is this the answer here shown on the sun? **743**

7. When finding the difference 'tween Six point two three, And eighty point three, Is this the answer you can see? **76·2**

NOW TRY THIS!

- **Make up some verses of your own for a partner to check using inverses.**

Teachers' note At the start of the lesson discuss the meaning of the word inverse and determine which operations are inverse to which. Demonstrate how calculations can be checked using the answer and the inverse calculation, for example to check 354 – 32 = 332 we can add 332 and 32 to see if the answer is 354.

A Lesson for Every Day
Maths
10–11 Years
© A&C Black

Cuboid crazy: 1

The vertices of this cuboid have been labelled.

A face can be described using the four letters of its corners. This face is **AEHD**.

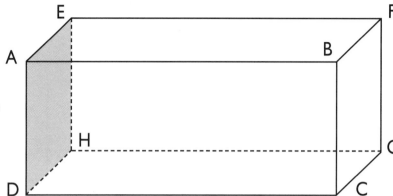

• **Write whether each statement is** | true | **or** | false |.

1. AEHD is perpendicular to EFGH.

true

2. FGCB is parallel to AEFB.

_____

3. HGCD is perpendicular to FGCB.

_____

4. ABCD is parallel to AEFB.

_____

5. EFGH is perpendicular to HGCD.

_____

6. EFGH is parallel to ABCD.

_____

7. ABCD is perpendicular to AEFB.

_____

8. AEFB is parallel to DHGC.

_____

9. BFGC is perpendicular to AEHD.

_____

10. AEHD is parallel to BFGC.

_____

NOW TRY THIS!

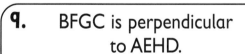

• **Write three true statements of your own.**

Teachers' note Provide the children with a cuboid to hold and turn. Alternatively, they could construct a cuboid from a coloured net to enable them to examine the different coloured faces.

A Lesson for Every Day
Maths
10–11 Years
© **A&C Black**

Cuboid crazy: 2

The vertices of this cuboid have been labelled.

An edge can be described using the two letters at each end. This edge is **FG**.

• **Write whether each statement is** | true | **or** | false |.

1. AE is perpendicular to EH.

true

2. EF is parallel to CG.

_____

3. HD is perpendicular to HG.

_____

4. AB is parallel to HG.

_____

5. AD is perpendicular to EF.

_____

6. EH is parallel to BC.

_____

7. AD is perpendicular to FB.

_____

8. AD is parallel to BC.

_____

9. HD is perpendicular to FG.

_____

10. HD is parallel to FB.

_____

11. BC is perpendicular to FB.

_____

12. CG is parallel to FE.

_____

NOW TRY THIS!

• **Write three true statements of your own.**

Teachers' note Provide the children with a cuboid to hold and turn. Ensure they understand that lines or edges that are perpendicular might not cross or touch in a diagram or shape, but that if one or other of them was extended, then they would cross or touch at right angles to each other.

A Lesson for Every Day
Maths
10-11 Years
© A&C Black

Path of truth

• Play this game with a partner.

☆ Take turns to roll the dice and move your counter.

☆ If the statement you land on is true, move forwards one place.
  If the statement is false, move backwards one place.

☆ The first player to cross the finish line is the winner.

You need a dice and two counters.

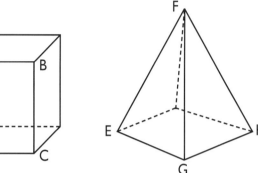

Shape a

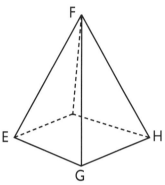

Shape b

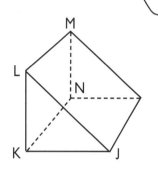

Shape c

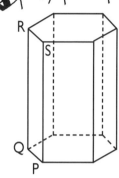

Shape d

Start	Shape **a** has **eight** edges perpendicular to AB.	Shape **b** has **no** parallel faces.	Shape **b** has **no** parallel edges.	Shape **a** has **one** face parallel to the face ABCD.	Shape **c** has **one** face parallel to the face JKL.
	Shape **c** has only **one** edge parallel to LM.	Shape **a** has **six** faces perpendicular to ABCD.	Shape **c** has **three** faces perpendicular to JKL.	Shape **c** has only **one** edge parallel to KL.	Shape **d** has **five** edges parallel to QR.
	Shape **a** has **one** face parallel to ABCD.	Shape **b** has **no** edges parallel to GH.	Shape **c** has **three** edges perpendicular to LM.	Shape **a** has **eight** edges perpendicular to CD.	Shape **b** has **no** edges perpendicular to GH.
	Shape **b** has **one** edge perpendicular to EF.	Shape **b** has **no** perpendicular faces.	Shape **d** has **six** edges perpendicular to RS.	Shape **b** has **one** edge perpendicular to EG.	Shape **d** has **no** faces parallel to PQRS.
	Shape **a** has only **two** edges parallel to AB.	Shape **d** has **no** edges parallel to PQ.	Shape **c** has **three** faces perpendicular to KLMN.	Every face on Shape **d** has a parallel face.	Every face on Shape **c** has a parallel face.	**Finish**

Teachers' note As an extension, ask the children to write six true statements of their own about parallel and perpendicular edges/faces in shapes a to d.

A Lesson for Every Day
Maths
10–11 Years
© A&C Black

Cut it out!

Each of these shapes can be cut into two pieces and rearranged to make a square.

The pieces do not have to be the same shape or size. They must <u>not</u> be turned face down.

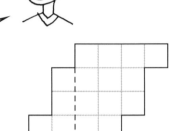

- **Draw dotted lines to predict where each shape can be cut.**

1.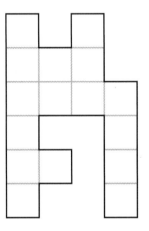

2.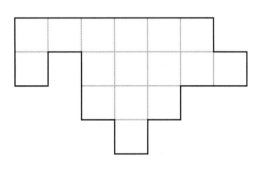

4.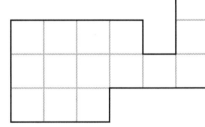

3.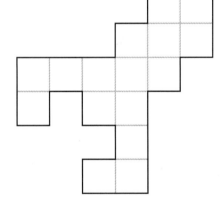

6.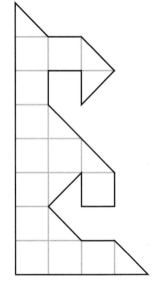

5.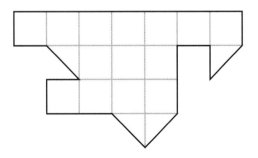

- **Cut out the pieces to check your predictions.**

Teachers' note Encourage the children to use squared paper to test their predictions before they cut the shapes into two pieces. They should then glue the pieces arranged as squares onto paper as a recording sheet. As an extension, the children can used squared paper to make their own puzzles for others to solve.

A Lesson for Every Day
Maths
10–11 Years
© A&C Black

House building

Christos is building a house.

There are many jobs that he needs to do.

- **Use the clues to decide in what order he must do the jobs. Then, rewrite his 'jobs to do' list.**

Jobs to do

A garden wall rebuilt

B plumbing installed

C walls plastered

D sand moved

E electrics fitted

F cement delivered

G garden wall knocked down

H foundations dug

Jobs to do

H   foundations dug

_____ _____

_____ _____

_____ _____

_____ _____

_____ _____

_____ _____

_____ _____

Clues

- The garden wall must be knocked down (G) before the cement can be delivered (F).
- The sand must be moved (D) before the wall can be knocked down (G).
- The electrics must be fitted (E) before the walls are plastered (C).
- The foundations must be dug first (H).
- The plumbing must be installed (B) before the electrics (E).
- The final job is rebuilding the garden wall (A).
- The plumbing is installed (B) after the cement is delivered (F).

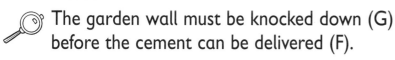

NOW TRY THIS!

- **Write an explanation to tell someone else how you solved this puzzle.**

Teachers' note Encourage the children to read through all the clues first. Provide scrap paper and encourage the children to use the letters to help them to organise the jobs into the correct order, before rewriting the 'jobs to do' list.

A Lesson for Every Day
Maths
10–11 Years
© A&C Black

Logical thinking

- **Use the clues to help you colour each pattern in the correct way.**

Work with a partner.

1

No circle is yellow.
Yellow is between two reds.
There are three greens in a row.
One circle is pink.
Under one green is a blue.

2

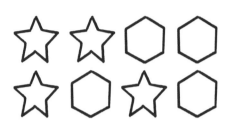

Blue is not next to a star.
No stars are the same colour.
Neither green is next to blue.
Two hexagons are red.
Yellow is between two reds.
Pink is next to a green hexagon.

3

Six shapes are green.
Between two greens is a red.
No pentagons are red.
One star is pink.
Yellow is not next to red or pink.
Between two greens is a yellow.

4

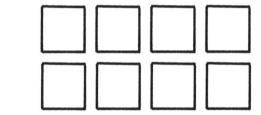

There are eight different colours: red, orange, yellow, green, blue, pink, white and purple.
Red is not next to pink or blue or orange.
Orange is above pink and to the right of blue.
Green is not next to white or red.
Yellow is above purple and to the right of red.

NOW TRY THIS!

- **Make up some colour puzzles of your own for a partner to solve.**

Teachers' note Ask the children to work in pairs to solve these puzzles and provide them with a range of coloured pencils. Before colouring their final solutions they should be encouraged to check that each clue works. Ensure that the children realise that same shapes are not necessarily the same colour.

A Lesson for Every Day
Maths
10–11 Years
© A&C Black

Equation persuasion

1 Mark each symbol equation with a ✔ or a ✘ to show whether it is **true** or **false** for the numbers shown.

 3   7   4   12   10

a 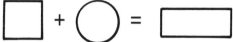 □ + ○ = ▭

b ○ − △ = □

c  ⬠ ÷ □ = △

d  □ + □ + △ = ▭

e 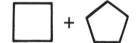 □ + ⬠ + ⬠ − ○ − ▭ = ▭

f  (○ − □) × □ = ⬠

2 Write four more symbol equations that are **true** for the numbers above.

NOW TRY THIS!

- **Is it possible to find a different set of numbers to represent the shapes so that all the statements on the page are still true?**

Teachers' note Encourage the children to use trial and improvement strategies for the extension activity, for example by first doubling the numbers and seeing whether the statements are true, adjusting where necessary to see whether all statements can be made to work.

A Lesson for Every Day
Maths
10–11 Years
© A&C Black

Animal magic

- **Work with a partner to solve these puzzles.**

1 In this hat there are some rabbits and some doves.
There are 12 legs and 8 wings.

a How many rabbits? _____

b How many doves? _____

2 In this hat there are some rabbits and some doves.
There are 26 legs and 16 eyes.

a How many rabbits? _____

b How many doves? _____

3 In this hat there are some rabbits and some snakes.
There are 20 legs and 14 eyes.

a How many rabbits? _____

b How many snakes? _____

4 In this hat there are some snakes and some doves.
There are 14 wings and 24 eyes.

a How many snakes? _____

b How many doves? _____

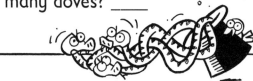

5 In this hat there are some rabbits and some snakes.
There are 24 legs and 20 eyes.

a How many rabbits? _____

b How many snakes? _____

6 In this hat there are some rabbits and some doves.
There are 20 eyes and 34 legs.

a How many rabbits? _____

b How many doves? _____

- **With your partner, write an explanation of how to solve this type of problem.**

NOW TRY THIS!

- **Make up your own puzzles using cats, fish and birds, and tails, eyes and legs.**

Teachers' note Discuss the number of eyes, wings and legs that the animals on this page have. For the extension, it is assumed that fish and birds each have one tail. Encourage the children to solve these puzzles algebraically.

A Lesson for Every Day
Maths
10–11 Years
© A&C Black

Grid riddles

The same calculation is done on each row of numbers in a grid.

- Fill in the missing numbers and equations.

1 | A + B = C

A	B	C
5	5	10
3	8	
4	9	
12	7	

2 | A − B = C

A	B	C
20	6	14
15	3	
9	1	
100	25	

3 | A × B = C

A	B	C
2	7	14
5	9	
8	4	
3	6	

4 | A × 2 − B = C

A	B	C
5	3	7
7	4	
9	11	
24	15	

5 | (A + B) × 2 = C

A	B	C
7	6	26
19	11	
16	12	
100	25	

6 | B ÷ A = C

A	B	C
3	9	3
9	18	
5	25	
25	75	

7

A	B	C
11	25	14
7	15	8
9	11	2
17	24	

8

A	B	C
10	6	26
15	4	34
5	75	85
100	25	

9

A	B	C
50	10	20
70	40	15
13	7	3
24	10	

NOW TRY THIS!

- Make up a grid riddle of your own for a partner to solve.

Teachers' note The equations or numbers could be altered to provide differentiation. Encourage the children to describe the relationships between the numbers and also to describe any patterns that they notice.

A Lesson for Every Day
Maths
10-11 Years
© A&C Black

Robot squares

- **Cut out the cards and play 'Snap' with a partner.**

1^2	2^2	3^2	4^2	5^2	6^2
7^2	8^2	9^2	10^2	11^2	12^2
1×1	2×2	3×3	4×4	5×5	6×6
7×7	8×8	9×9	10×10	11×11	12×12
1	4	9	16	25	36
49	64	81	100	121	144
one squared	two squared	three squared	four squared	five squared	six squared
seven squared	eight squared	nine squared	ten squared	eleven squared	twelve squared

Teachers' note Enlarge this sheet to A3 when photocopying. These cards can be used by children to play pairs, where cards are placed face down on a table and two turned over at a time. If they match, the cards are kept. If not they are turned face down again. The cards could also be used for an individual sorting activity.

A Lesson for Every Day
Maths
10–11 Years
© A&C Black

Division testing cards

- **Cut out Tests A, B and C and write the answers.**
- **Cut out strips A, B and C to check whether your answers are correct.**

Test A	Test B	Test C	A	B	C
8·1 ÷ 9 = _____	1·6 ÷ 4 = _____	1·4 ÷ 7 = _____	0·9	0·4	0·2
3·5 ÷ 7 = _____	2·4 ÷ 8 = _____	3·6 ÷ 6 = _____	0·5	0·3	0·6
6·4 ÷ 8 = _____	3·0 ÷ 5 = _____	0 ÷ 0·3 = _____	0·8	0·6	0
6·0 ÷ 10 = _____	1·6 ÷ 4 = _____	4·0 ÷ 5 = _____	0·6	0·4	0·8
1·6 ÷ 2 = _____	1·8 ÷ 3 = _____	4·9 ÷ 7 = _____	0·8	0·6	0·7
1·2 ÷ 2 = _____	3·6 ÷ 4 = _____	7·2 ÷ 8 = _____	0·6	0·9	0·9
4·2 ÷ 7 = _____	1·5 ÷ 3 = _____	4·5 ÷ 5 = _____	0·6	0·5	0·9
3·6 ÷ 4 = _____	3·2 ÷ 8 = _____	5·6 ÷ 8 = _____	0·9	0·4	0·7
2·7 ÷ 3 = _____	1·2 ÷ 6 = _____	8·0 ÷ 10 = _____	0·9	0·2	0·8
2·0 ÷ 4 = _____	2·8 ÷ 7 = _____	6·3 ÷ 7 = _____	0·5	0·4	0·9
4·5 ÷ 5 = _____	4·8 ÷ 6 = _____	8·1 ÷ 9 = _____	0·9	0·8	0·9
1·4 ÷ 2 = _____	1·2 ÷ 3 = _____	3·5 ÷ 5 = _____	0·7	0·4	0·7
3·6 ÷ 6 = _____	2·4 ÷ 6 = _____	6·4 ÷ 8 = _____	0·6	0·4	0·8
3·0 ÷ 6 = _____	1·8 ÷ 9 = _____	3·5 ÷ 7 = _____	0·5	0·2	0·5
4·0 ÷ 8 = _____	2·1 ÷ 7 = _____	1·6 ÷ 8 = _____	0·5	0·3	0·2
4·9 ÷ 7 = _____	2·5 ÷ 5 = _____	1·8 ÷ 2 = _____	0·7	0·5	0·9
7·2 ÷ 8 = _____	5·4 ÷ 6 = _____	4·2 ÷ 6 = _____	0·9	0·9	0·7
4·5 ÷ 9 = _____	1·2 ÷ 4 = _____	3·6 ÷ 9 = _____	0·5	0·3	0·4
5·6 ÷ 7 = _____	3·5 ÷ 5 = _____	2·0 ÷ 10 = _____	0·8	0·7	0·2
2·4 ÷ 8 = _____	2·0 ÷ 5 = _____	1·0 ÷ 5 = _____	0·3	0·4	0·2

Teachers' note These cards can be cut out and used as testing cards for all the division facts for decimals corresponding to those of the times tables up to 10 × 10. Encourage the children to note each time they try a test which answers they got wrong or could not work out and to learn them.

A Lesson for Every Day
Maths
10–11 Years
© A&C Black

71

Conveyor belts

- Choose a number between 50 and 100 and follow the diagram from the start.
- Use a calculator to help you find which numbers are prime and which are not.

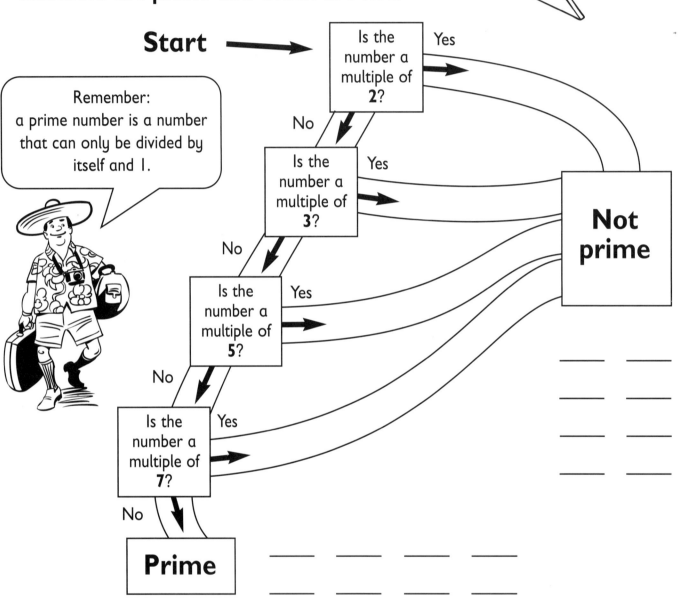

Start ➝

Remember: a prime number is a number that can only be divided by itself and 1.

Is the number a multiple of **2**? — Yes ➝

No ↓

Is the number a multiple of **3**? — Yes ➝

No ↓

Is the number a multiple of **5**? — Yes ➝

No ↓

Is the number a multiple of **7**? — Yes ➝

No ↓

Not prime

— — — —

— — — —

— — — —

— — — —

Prime

— — — — — —

— — — — — —

NOW TRY THIS!

To test numbers between 100 and 140 you must also check whether the number is a multiple of 11.

- Tick which of these numbers are prime.

101 ☐   119 ☐   121 ☐   123 ☐   127 ☐   131 ☐   137 ☐

Teachers' note Encourage the children to write the numbers chosen on the lines to show whether they are prime or not prime. Demonstrate how to use a calculator to divide the number by 2, 3, 5 or 7 and to see whether the answer is a whole number. Ensure the children understand that if it is a multiple of the number there will be no remainder after the division.

A Lesson for Every Day
Maths
10–11 Years
© A&C Black

Prime suspect

The Polka Dot Kid is hiding and the police are trying to find him.

- Shade the dots for all the numbers below that are prime numbers . Then join them in order, from smallest to largest, to find where he is.

NOW TRY THIS!

- Choose two prime numbers and add them together. Can you find an answer that is a square number?

Teachers' note Ensure the children understand that a prime number has only two factors, itself and 1. They could use a copy of the 'Conveyor belts' and a calculator to help them determine which numbers are prime. Discuss the nature of prime numbers, for example that they are all odd, except for the prime number 2.

A Lesson for Every Day
Maths
10-11 Years
© A&C Black

Sponsored sports

Hawsker school is having a sponsored sports day for charity.

- **Use a calculator to answer these questions.**

Work with a partner.

1. Kim is sponsored 5p for every 10 cm she jumps in the long jump. She jumps 4·3 m. How much does she raise? _____

2. Leon is sponsored £5 to run 20 laps around the field. He must run it in less than 18 minutes to raise the money. If his lap average time is 45 seconds, will he raise the money? _____

3. Emma is sponsored to run as many laps around the field as she can. She is sponsored 75p per lap. How many laps does she run if she raises £20.25? _____

4. Freddie throws a beanbag. For every 10 cm over 3·5 m that he throws it he is sponsored 37p. How much will he raise if he throws the beanbag 480 cm? _____

5. Jasmine also throws a beanbag. For every 5 cm over 4 m that she throws it she is sponsored 65p. How much will she raise if she throws the beanbag 4·75 m? _____

6. Urvi is sponsored 18p for every 20 cm she jumps in the high jump. She jumps 2·6 m. How much does she raise? _____

7. (a) Billy is sponsored to run as many laps around the field as he can. He is sponsored 68p per lap plus an extra £4.50 if he runs more than 25 laps. How much does he raise if he runs 23 laps? _____

(b) How much does Billy raise if he runs 26 laps? _____

NOW TRY THIS!

- **Find the total amount of money raised by the children. (Billy runs 26 laps.)** _____

Teachers' note Provide the children with calculators for these questions and encourage them to discuss each situation with a partner.

A Lesson for Every Day
Maths
10-11 Years
© A&C Black

- **Cut out the shape tiles carefully and write the name of the shape on the back of each tile.**

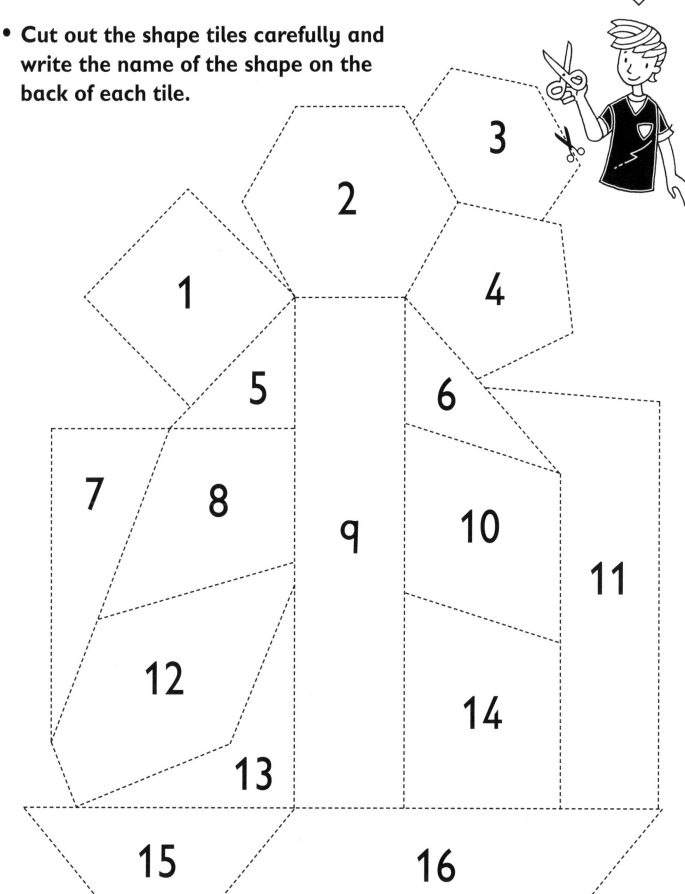

Teachers' note Use in conjunction with 'Shape sort: 2'. The sheet could be copied onto card or enlarged to A3 size. The shapes could also be laminated, to create a more permanent resource.

A Lesson for Every Day
Maths
10–11 Years
© A&C Black

75

Shape sort: 2

- **Record each shape in the correct position on each Venn diagram.**

You need the shape tiles from Shape sort: 1.

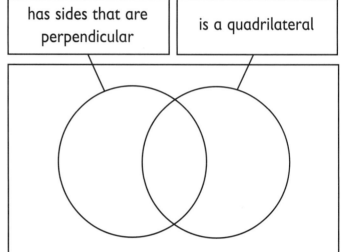

has at least one pair of parallel sides   has at least one right angle

has sides that are perpendicular   is a quadrilateral

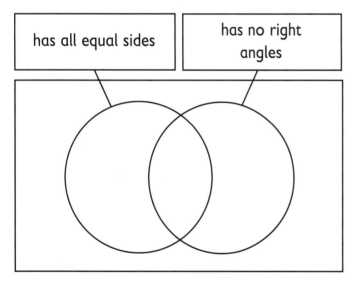

has all equal sides   has no right angles

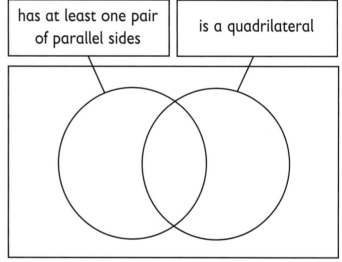

has at least one pair of parallel sides   is a quadrilateral

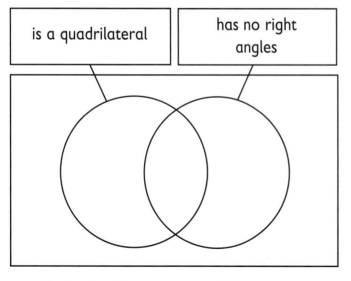

is a quadrilateral   has no right angles

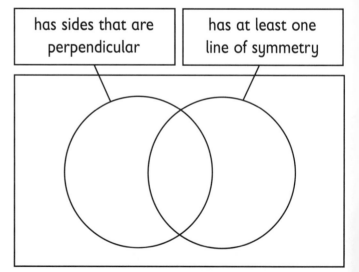

has sides that are perpendicular   has at least one line of symmetry

Teachers' note Use in conjunction with 'Shape sort: 1'. At the start of the lesson, demonstrate how to sort shapes onto a Venn diagram, using different criteria. The sheet could be enlarged and split into six different sorting activities, one per group, if preferred. The children could compare the solutions to the second and fifth diagrams, and discuss them.

A Lesson for Every Day
Maths
10–11 Years
© A&C Black

3-D detective

- **Look at these shapes.**

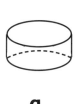 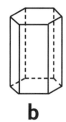 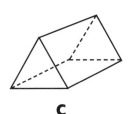 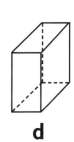 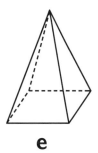 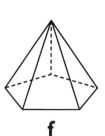

a   b   c   d   e   f

- **Which of the shapes above matches each description?**
- **Write the letter of the shape in the magnifying glass.**

1. This shape has three pairs of parallel faces.

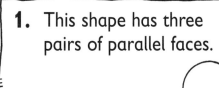

2. This shape has only one pair of parallel faces. Some of its edges are perpendicular.

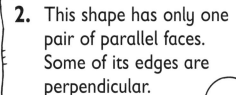

3. None of this shape's faces is parallel and none of its edges is perpendicular.

4. Each of this shape's faces has a parallel face but not every touching edge is perpendicular.

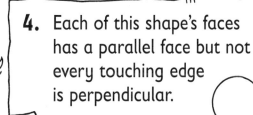

5. Some of this shape's edges are perpendicular but it has only two pairs of parallel edges.

6. This shape has one pair of parallel faces and one pair of curved parallel edges.

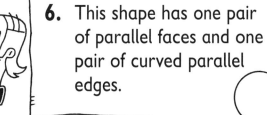

NOW TRY THIS!

- **Make up some descriptions of your own about the edges and faces of these shapes.**

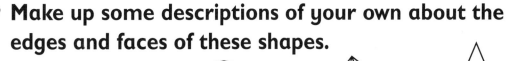

Teachers' note Ideally, provide the children with the matching solid shapes so that they can hold and examine them. For the extension activity, encourage the children to write a description that could not apply to any of the other shapes. They could then swap descriptions with a partner.

A Lesson for Every Day
Maths
10–11 Years
© A&C Black

Tetrahedra

• **Copy this net of a tetrahedron four times.**

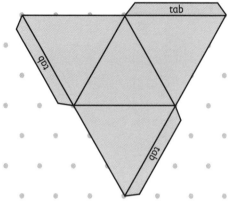

Do **not** shade the nets.

• **Cut out the nets and fold them to make five tetrahedra.**

NOW TRY THIS!

• **Stick each white tetrahedron to the face of the grey one. What shape do you make?** _____

• **How many faces, edges and vertices does it have?**

_____

Teachers' note Ideally, this sheet should be copied onto thin card. The children will need scissors and glue (or transparent tape).

A Lesson for Every Day
Maths
10-11 Years
© A&C Black

Table challenges

Challenge 1

✳ A cup of tea and three cakes cost £3.
✳ Two cups of tea and two cakes cost £3.60.
✳ Three cups of tea and one cake cost £4.20.

• **Fill in the table to show the cost of any number of teas and cakes.**

Number of teas	Number of cakes				
	0	1	2	3	4
0					
1				£3	
2			£3.60		
3		£4.20			
4					

Challenge 2

✳ A magazine and two cans of cola cost £1.85.
✳ Two magazines and three cans of cola cost £3.15.
✳ Four magazines and four cans of cola cost £5.20.

• **Complete the table.**

Number of magazines	Number of cans of cola				
	0	1	2	3	4
0					
1					
2					
3					
4					

Teachers' note This activity can help the children to realise the value of tabulating information, as it becomes easier to see patterns in the numbers and, therefore, easier to spot errors. Further questions of this type could be given and the children could construct their own tables.

A Lesson for Every Day
Maths
10-11 Years
© A&C Black

Square numbers

- **Look at each statement. Find out whether the statement is**
  ⎡ always true ⎤ , ⎡ sometimes true ⎤ **, or** ⎡ never true ⎤ **.**
- **Show your working and give examples.**

1
> I take an odd number
> and square it.
> The answer is one more than
> a multiple of 4.

2
> I add two consecutive
> square numbers.
> The answer is odd.

3
> I square two consecutive whole
> numbers and find the difference.
> The difference is the sum of the
> two consecutive whole numbers.

4
> I take a multiple of 3
> and square it.
> The answer is a multiple of 9.

5
> I take an odd square number
> and find the sum of its digits.
> The answer is an odd number.

6
> I find the product of two
> consecutive odd numbers
> and add 1.
> The answer is a square number.

Teachers' note Begin by writing a list of the numbers to 20, and ask the children to find the squares of each number. Leave these on the board for the children to refer to when tackling this activity. Encourage the children to justify their thoughts and to say whether they can be absolutely certain when they say a statement is always true.

A Lesson for Every Day
Maths
10–11 Years
© A&C Black

A general rule

The questions in each row are similar.

- **Explain in words how you could solve them.**

1

How many days are there in 12 weeks?

How many days are there in 29 weeks?

How many days are there in 106 weeks?

2

How many months are there in 4 years?

How many months are there in 9 years?

How many months are there in 16 years?

3

How many weeks are there in 8 years?

How many weeks are there in 11 years?

How many weeks are there in 15 years?

4

DVDs cost £11 each. How much will 6 DVDs cost?

DVDs cost £11 each. How much will 12 DVDs cost?

DVDs cost £11 each. How much will 22 DVDs cost?

5

How much change will I get from £50 if I buy 3 CDs costing £6 each?

How much change will I get from £50 if I buy 5 CDs costing £6 each?

How much change will I get from £50 if I buy 7 CDs costing £6 each?

NOW TRY THIS!

- **Write a formula for each row using the letter *n* to stand for the number of days, months, weeks, DVDs or CDs.**

Teachers' note Encourage the children to begin to see how a formula can be used to describe a particular question type, for example rather than always giving the individual question 12 x 7, 29 x 7, 106 x 7, we can generalise and say 'Multiply the number of weeks by 7', or better still say 'The number of days = 7n, where n is the number of weeks'.

A Lesson for Every Day
Maths
10–11 Years
© A&C Black

Formula fun

• **Write an expression or formula to help solve each problem.**

1 Jon has 60 pence and is given *n* pence. How much does he have now?

2 Mrs Mason bakes *x* cakes. She eats three of them. How many are left?

3 Ian eats *b* bags of crisps. Pauline eats twice as many. How many does Pauline eat?

4 Dinesh scores *p* goals. Jake scores half as many. How many does Jake score?

5 Jack spends £*a* in the shop and Josh spends £*b*. How much do they spend altogether?

6 In a test, Tom answers 5*x* questions and gets *x* questions right. How many does he get wrong?

7 Lucy spends £*y* on magazines and £6 on books. How much does she spend altogether?

8 Jo is given £*x* for her birthday. She gives £*y* to her brother. How much does she have left?

9 There are 19 people on a bus. Another 7 people get on and *x* people get off. How many people are on the bus now?

10 Charlie has £12 but loses £*y*. How much does she have left?

NOW TRY THIS!

• **Make up a story of your own using *x* and *y*. Ask a partner to find its formula.**

82

Teachers' note Ensure the children understand that a letter can stand for any number and that if in one question *x* stands for 5, then *x* can represent another number elsewhere.

A Lesson for Every Day
Maths
10–11 Years
© A&C Black

Square secrets

- **Answer the questions and use the key below to find the words for 'square' in other languages.**

German

30 × 30	7²	90²	110²	120²	90 × 90	60 squared
900						
q						

Dutch

100²	20 squared	11²	120 × 120	50²	90 squared	12²	60 × 60

Spanish

80 × 80	7 × 7	90 squared	110²	120 squared	90²	110 × 110	70²

Danish

40 × 40	20²	120²	50 squared	90²	12 × 12	60 squared

Key

8100	3600	6400	49	10 000	4900	1600
a	t	c	u	v	o	f

900	121	2500	12 100	400	14 400	144
q	e	k	d	i	r	n

Teachers' note This activity provides an opportunity for children to practise recalling and deriving quickly the squares of multiples of 10 corresponding to the squares of numbers to 12.

A Lesson for Every Day
Maths
10–11 Years
© A&C Black

Magic squares

• **Multiply each number in this grid by the numbers below to create magic squares.**

4	3	8
9	5	1
2	7	6

× 0·7

2·8		

_____

× 0·8

_____

× 0·6

_____

× 0·4

_____

× 0·3

_____

× 0·9

_____

NOW TRY THIS!

• **Multiply the decimals in this grid by 2.**

4·9	4·7	5·7
5·9	5·1	4·3
4·5	5·5	5·3

9·8		

• **Does it still make a magic square?** _____

Teachers' note The main activity provides practice in finding products of decimals corresponding to multiplication facts up to 10 × 10. Ensure the children understand that a magic square is special as its rows, columns and diagonals all have the same total. Encourage them to write this total on the line beneath each grid.

A Lesson for Every Day
Maths
10-11 Years
© A&C Black

Prime factor compactor

This machine takes only prime numbers and puts them together by multiplying them.

The prime numbers can be used more than once.

2

3

5

7

11

13

$12 = 2 \times 2 \times 3$

$10 = 2 \times 5$

$54 = 3 \times 3 \times 3 \times 2$

• **Investigate what numbers can be made.**

_____   _____

_____   _____

_____   _____

_____   _____

_____   _____

_____   _____

_____   _____

Numbers I have made:

_____

NOW TRY THIS!

• **Do you think it is possible to make all the numbers up to 50 in this way?** _____

• **Talk to a partner and explain your thinking.**

Teachers' note Write a list of the following prime numbers on the board for children to refer to: 2, 3, 5, 7, 11, 13, 17, 19, 23, 29 … Remind children that a prime number has only two factors, itself and 1, for example 2 is a prime number as it only has the factors 1 and 2, 5 is a prime number as it only has the factors 1 and 5.

A Lesson for Every Day
Maths
10–11 Years
© A&C Black

American football

The prime numbers on each footballer are multiplied together.

• **Write the answer to each multiplication.**

1.
$\boxed{18}$ =

2.
$\boxed{}$ =

3.
$\boxed{}$ =

4.
$\boxed{}$ =

5.
$\boxed{}$ =

6.
$\boxed{}$ =

7.
$\boxed{}$ =

8.
$\boxed{}$ =

9.
$\boxed{}$ =

NOW TRY THIS!

• **Write the correct prime numbers for these.**

(a) $\boxed{12}$ = $\square$ × $\square$ × $\square$ (b) $\boxed{20}$ = $\square$ × $\square$ × $\square$

(c) $\boxed{50}$ = $\square$ × $\square$ × $\square$ (d) $\boxed{28}$ = $\square$ × $\square$ × $\square$

(e) $\boxed{98}$ = $\square$ × $\square$ × $\square$ (f) $\boxed{125}$ = $\square$ × $\square$ × $\square$

(g) $\boxed{16}$ = $\square$ × $\square$ × $\square$ × $\square$

Teachers' note Write a list of the following prime numbers on the board for children to refer to: 2, 3, 5, 7, 11 … Remind children that a prime number has only two factors, itself and 1, for example 2 is a prime number as it only has the factors 1 and 2, 5 is a prime number as it only has the factors 1 and 5. To provide more variety, the numbers could be altered. See the notes on the activity on page 12 for details.

A Lesson for Every Day
Maths
10-11 Years
© A&C Black

Primes, squares and multiples

Square number	Multiple of 10 Prime number

- **Fill in the shapes below to make true statements.**
- **Check the correct type of number is entered into each shape.**

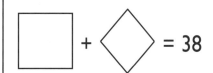

□ + ◇ = 38   ◇ + ◯ = 91   □ + ◯ = 65

□ + □ = 97   □ + ◯ = 76   ◇ + ◇ = 42

◇ + □ = 66   ◇ + ◯ = 72   □ + ◯ = 104

□ + □ = ◇   ◇ + ◯ = □   □ + ◯ = ◇

NOW TRY THIS!

- **Which of these statements are possible to complete?**

◇ + ◇ = ◇   ◯ + ◯ = □

□ + □ = □   ◯ + ◯ = ◇

◇ + ◇ = □   □ + ◯ = □

Teachers' note Ensure the children understand that there may be many different ways of correctly completing each question. Encourage them to explain why one of the statements is not possible in the extension activity.

A Lesson for Every Day
Maths
10-11 Years
© A&C Black

Just for pets

- **Tick which item on the shelf is the best value for money. Show all your workings.**

Use a calculator.

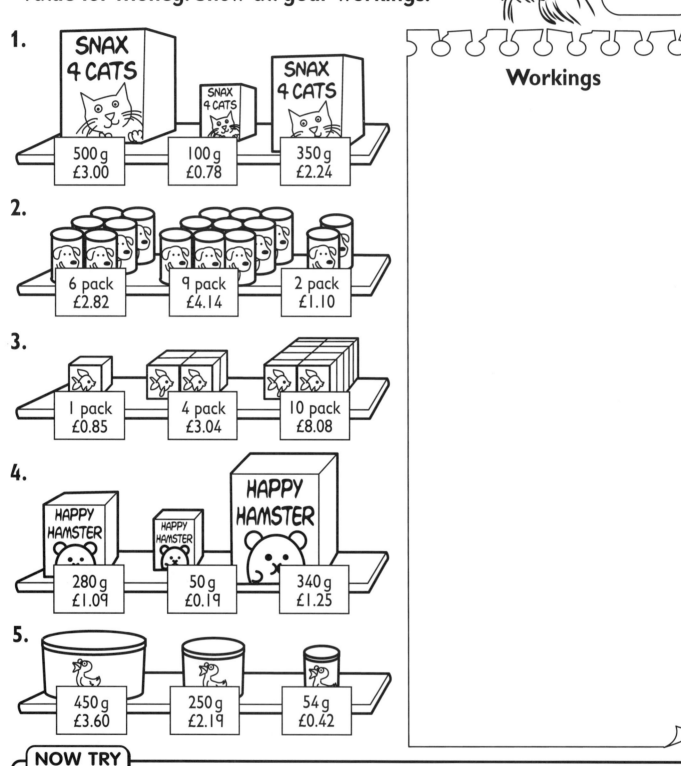

Workings

1.

SNAX 4 CATS
500 g £3.00

SNAX 4 CATS
100 g £0.78

SNAX 4 CATS
350 g £2.24

2.

6 pack £2.82

9 pack £4.14

2 pack £1.10

3.

1 pack £0.85

4 pack £3.04

10 pack £8.08

4.

HAPPY HAMSTER
280 g £1.09

HAPPY HAMSTER
50 g £0.19

HAPPY HAMSTER
340 g £1.25

5.

450 g £3.60

250 g £2.19

54 g £0.42

NOW TRY THIS!

- **Make up some 'value for money' puzzles for a partner to solve.**

Teachers' note At the start of the lesson, demonstrate how value for money can be calculated by finding the cost per item or per gram.

A Lesson for Every Day
Maths
10–11 Years
© A&C Black

Cutting corners

- **Imagine that the marked corner of each 3-D shape is cut off to create an extra face on the 3-D shape.**
- **Write what shape the extra face would be.**

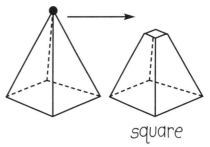

square

1.

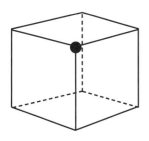

_____

2.

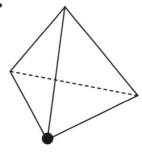

_____

3.

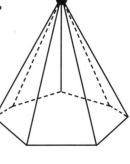

_____

4.

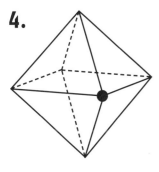

_____

5.

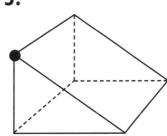

_____

6.

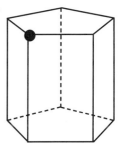

_____

7.

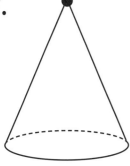

_____

8.

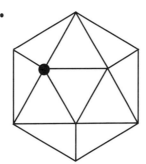

_____

9.

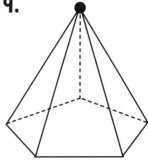

_____

NOW TRY THIS!

- **What do you notice about the shapes of the faces made by cutting off the tops of pyramids and cones?**

_____

Teachers' note Encourage the children to count the number of edges that meet at each vertex to help them predict or check their answers. The children should imagine making cuts that create regular shapes only. Note that the shape in question 8 is called an icosahedron as it has 20 faces. (In Greek, 'icosi' means 'twenty' and 'hedron' means 'faces'.)

A Lesson for Every Day
Maths
10-11 Years
© A&C Black

Compass mastery

- **Cut out the instruction cards below and follow one set of instructions at a time.**

You need scissors, a ruler and a pair of compasses.

How to draw a <u>regular hexagon</u>

☆ Draw a circle with the compasses. (Don't change the width of the compasses!)

☆ Draw a dot on the edge of the circle.

☆ Place the point of the compasses on the dot and mark another point on the edge of the circle.

☆ Keep going like this until six points are marked on the edge.

☆ Join the points with a ruler.

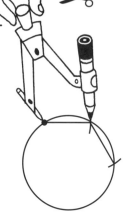

How to draw an <u>equilateral triangle</u>

☆ Draw a dot on the paper.

☆ Place the point of the compasses on the dot and mark another dot. (Don't move the compasses!)

☆ Now draw an **arc** like this:

☆ Put the point on the other dot and draw another arc.

☆ Join the points with a ruler.

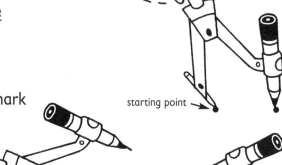

starting point

starting point

starting point

NOW TRY THIS!

- **On card, draw four equilateral triangles to form the net of a tetrahedron.**
- **Draw tabs and cut and fold the net to make a tetrahedron.**

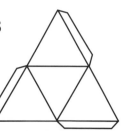

Teachers' note This activity provides an opportunity for the children to construct 2-D shapes with increasing accuracy. The children could work in pairs (see the notes on the activity on page 12). For the extension activity, the children will also need card, scissors and glue (or transparent tape).

A Lesson for Every Day
Maths
10–11 Years
© A&C Black

Dodecahedra

- **Cut out this net to make a regular** $\boxed{\text{dodecahedron}}$.
- **Look carefully at each vertex. Count how many edges meet at each vertex.**

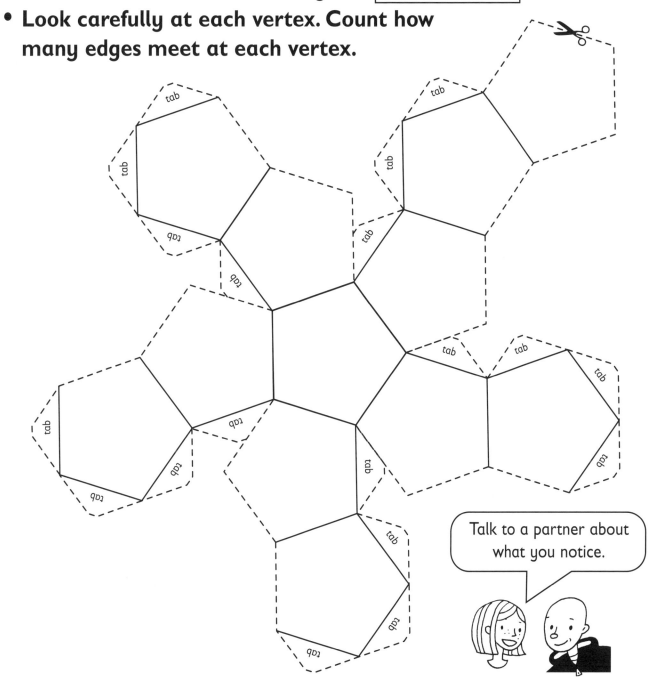

Talk to a partner about what you notice.

NOW TRY THIS!

This is also a net of a regular dodecahedron.

- **Draw as many different nets of this shape as you can.**

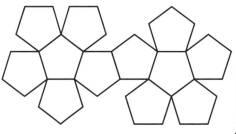

Use a regular pentagon as a template to draw round.

Teachers' note Explain that the word 'dodeca' means 'twelve' in Greek and 'hedron' means 'faces', so this shape is called a dodecahedron because it has 12 faces. The shape above is a regular dodecahedron, made from 12 regular pentagons. The children will need scissors and glue (or transparent tape). Ideally, this sheet should be copied onto thin card.

A Lesson for Every Day
Maths
10–11 Years
© A&C Black

Let's enquire: 1

- **Work with a partner.**
- **Read through the questions and choose one of them to work with.**

You need Let's enquire: 2.

Do most people in our class have hair longer than 10 cm?

Are girls more likely to own a mobile phone than boys?

What type of books do children in our class like to read?

Which is the most common bird in the school playground?

Are girls more likely to play a musical instrument than boys?

Are vegetarians more likely to own a pet than non-vegetarians?

- **Cut out your chosen question and stick it onto Let's enquire: 2.**

Teachers' note Use in conjunction with 'Let's enquire: 2'. Each pair chooses a question and then sticks it onto page 93. They then plan how they would go about answering the question. For the 'more likely' questions, discuss whether just asking children in their own class fully answers the question, for example it may be true for their class, but not for people of all ages.

A Lesson for Every Day
Maths
10–11 Years
© A&C Black

Let's enquire: 2

You are going to plan an investigation or survey.

- **Fill in the boxes below.**

Make sure you agree.

Stick your chosen question here.

How are we going to find out?
What resources will we need?
What do we think the results are likely to be?

- **If you need to design a recording sheet or a questionnaire:**

Think carefully about any questions you ask.

- ▶ Could they be misunderstood?
- ▶ What possible answers could be given?
- ▶ Do you need to suggest possible answers for people to choose from?

Think carefully about your recording sheet.

- ▶ Have you got enough space for recording the information?
- ▶ How quick will it be to fill in? Can you make it quicker?
- ▶ Have you extra space for writing any interesting comments?

Teachers' note Use in conjunction with 'Let's enquire: 1'. Discuss this planning sheet with the whole class before getting the children into pairs (or small groups if preferred). Ensure that they understand what is required and suggest different ways in which they could work, distribute responsibility in the work, record, and represent the information.

A Lesson for Every Day
Maths
10-11 Years
© A&C Black

Birthday survey: 1

- ## You are going to find out the answers to these questions:

> **A** Are more people in our class born in Spring and Summer than in Autumn and Winter?
>
> **B** Are more people in our class born at the beginning of a month than at the end of a month?
>
> **C** Which is the most common day of the week for people in our class to have their birthday this year?

- ## With a partner, decide how best to collect the information that will help you to answer <u>all three</u> questions.

- ## Write a description of what you have decided to do.

> Give as much detail as you can about the questions you will ask, how you will record the information, and what you will do with it. Use the back of this sheet if you need to.

NOW TRY THIS!

- ## Talk to other people in your class. Have they decided to collect the information in the same way or in different ways? What are the advantages and disadvantages of these ways?

Teachers' note Use in conjunction with 'Birthday survey: 2'. This worksheet encourages the children to realise that there are different ways of collecting this kind of data (see page 12 for more information). Provide the children with the opportunity to plan and decide upon their own collection methods without guidance, then discuss and compare their ideas as a whole class.

A Lesson for Every Day
Maths
10–11 Years
© A&C Black

Birthday survey: 2

- Imagine that you are reporting the results of your survey in a newspaper or magazine.
- Write an explanation of the purpose of your survey, what you did and how you carried it out. Include tables or graphs to show what you found out.

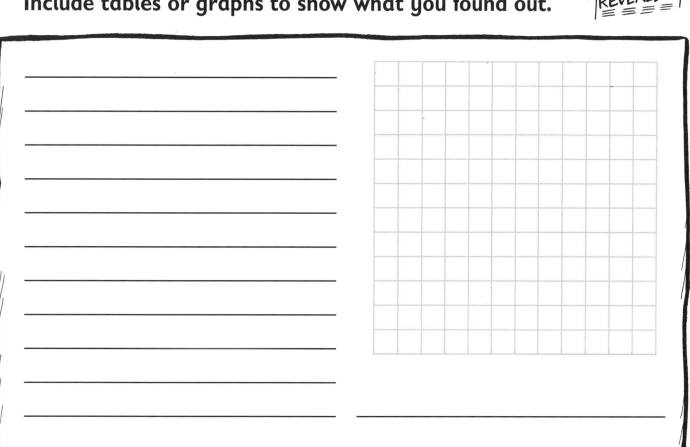

- If you were to do this survey again, what would you change?

NOW TRY THIS!

- On the back of this sheet, write four statements about your results.

Teachers' note Use in conjunction with 'Birthday survey: 1'. For the extension, encourage the children to use phrases like 'most common', 'least common', 'mode', 'range', 'mean' (where appropriate), and to choose a suitable means of representing the data in charts or tables.

A Lesson for Every Day
Maths
10–11 Years
© A&C Black

Finding out

- **With a partner, discuss how you could find the answers to the problems below.**

A How much water does our class use in one week?

B On average, which class at our school has the most amount of sleep per week?

C How many children attend our school? Is this different from the number when our school first opened?

D How many kilometres do I walk during a typical week?

- **Which is the easiest investigation to carry out?** ___
- **Why do you think so?** _____

_____

- **Which investigation is the most difficult to collect data for?** ___
- **Why do you think so?** _____

_____

- **Choose the investigation that you are most interested in.** ___
- **What data would you need to collect? How could you collect it?**

_____

_____

_____

Teachers' note If appropriate, the children could suggest their own lines of enquiry to investigate. Encourage them to think about whether the problems need refining and how to ensure accurate data collection.

A Lesson for Every Day
Maths
10–11 Years
© A&C Black

Testing times

Maisy's class took a test. There were 14 marks in total. The bar chart shows the children's scores.

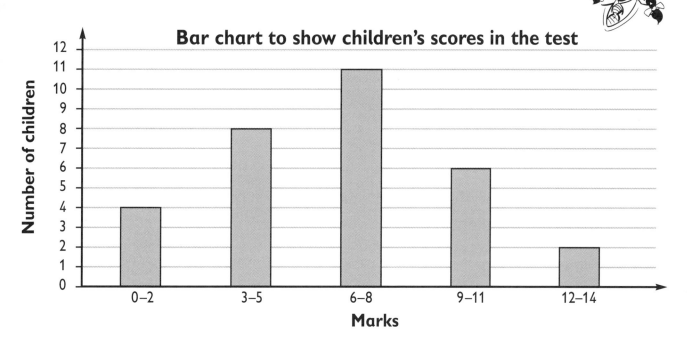

Bar chart to show children's scores in the test

(y-axis: Number of children, 0–12; x-axis: Marks; bars: 0–2 = 4, 3–5 = 8, 6–8 = 11, 9–11 = 6, 12–14 = 2)

- **Use the bar chart to answer these questions.**

1 How many children scored two marks or less? _____

2 How many children scored nine marks or more? _____

3 How many children were in the class altogether? _____

4 Does the data tell you Maisy's score in the test? _____

5 Do you think the data could be presented in another way?

Discuss your ideas with a partner.

NOW TRY THIS!

- **What do you notice about the shape of the bar chart?**

Talk to your partner about your ideas.

Teachers' note This activity focuses on the purpose of grouping data and helps the children to understand the strengths and limitations of doing this.

A Lesson for Every Day
Maths
10–11 Years
© A&C Black

You are what you eat

● **Answer the questions about the pie charts.**

1 How many different cake ingredients were used? ____

2 Which ingredient was:
  a the heaviest? _____
  b the lightest? _____

3 The total weight of the ingredients was 360 g. What was the weight of each ingredient?

  a margarine _____ g
  b sugar _____ g
  c fruit _____ g
  d eggs _____ g
  e flour _____ g

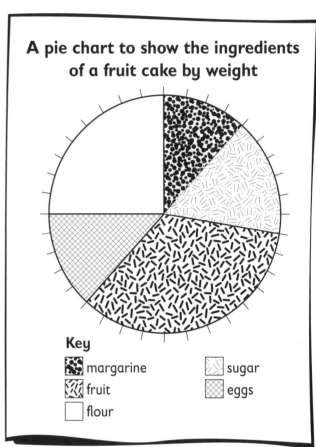

A pie chart to show the ingredients of a fruit cake by weight

Key
[▒] margarine   [▒] sugar
[▒] fruit   [▒] eggs
[ ] flour

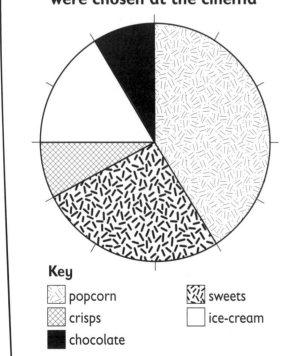

A pie chart to show which snacks were chosen at the cinema

Key
[▒] popcorn   [▒] sweets
[▒] crisps   [ ] ice-cream
[■] chocolate

4 24 children went to the cinema. What fraction had:
  a popcorn? _____
  b sweets? _____
  c crisps? _____
  d ice-cream? _____
  e chocolate? _____

5 How many children had:
  a popcorn? _____
  b sweets? _____
  c crisps? _____
  d ice-cream? _____
  e chocolate? _____

Teachers' note Ensure that the children understand the concept of proportion. Also check that they understand that a pie chart shows the size of one piece of data in relation to the whole, for example in the first pie chart, the sector for margarine shows the weight of the margarine compared to the weight of all the ingredients, and how one piece of data can be seen in the context of the whole.

A Lesson for Every Day
Maths
10–11 Years
© A&C Black

Home on the range: 1

You need the digital cards cut from Home on the range: 2.

I   Shuffle the cards.

I   Turn over two cards and make a two-digit number.

I   Repeat until you have made five two-digit numbers.

I   Write the numbers in order in the circles, smallest to largest.

I   Calculate the **range** and write it in the square.

A   ◯ ◯ ◯ ◯ ◯   □

I   Repeat to make six more sets of data.

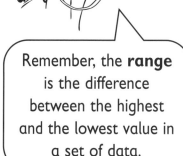

Remember, the **range** is the difference between the highest and the lowest value in a set of data.

B   ◯ ◯ ◯ ◯ ◯   □

C   ◯ ◯ ◯ ◯ ◯   □

D   ◯ ◯ ◯ ◯ ◯   □

E   ◯ ◯ ◯ ◯ ◯   □

F   ◯ ◯ ◯ ◯ ◯   □

G   ◯ ◯ ◯ ◯ ◯   □

• **Answer these questions about your data.**

1 Which set of data has the largest range? ___

2 Which set of data has the smallest range? ___

3 Why is the range useful? _____

Teachers' note Use in conjunction with 'Home on the range: 2'. The children could work in pairs for this activity. Once a set of numbers has been made, the digit cards are replaced and shuffled on the table. As an extension, ask the children to work out the missing number for this set of data, where the range is 74: 6, 32, 55, 70, (80).

A Lesson for Every Day
Maths
10–11 Years
© A&C Black

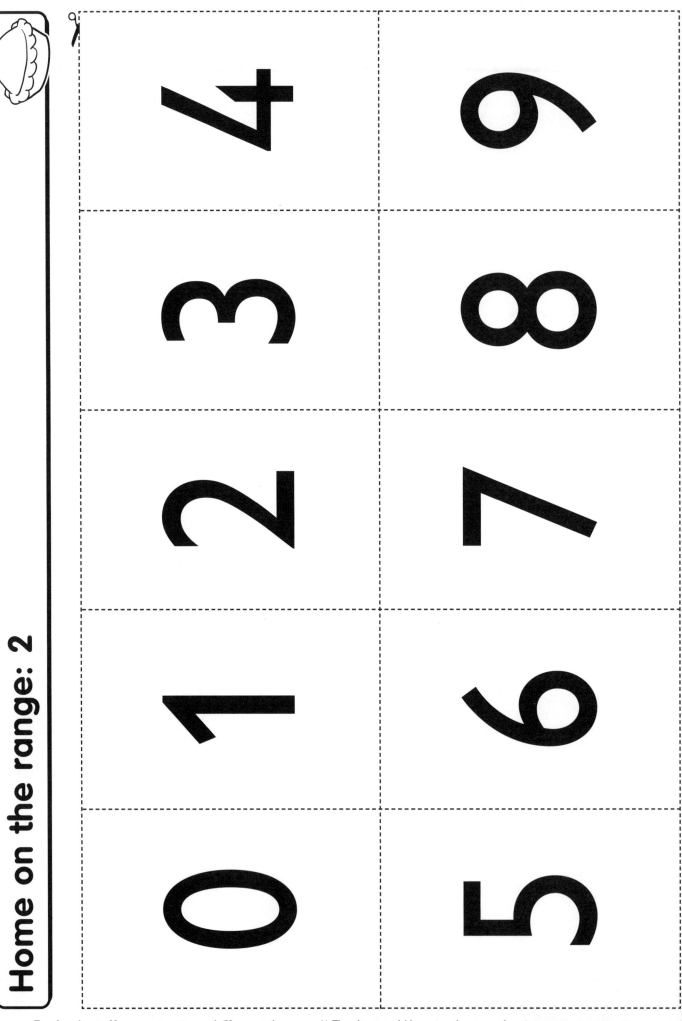

Teachers' note Use in conjunction with 'Home on the range: 1'. The sheet could be printed onto card and laminated to provide a useful classroom resource.

A Lesson for Every Day
Maths
10–11 Years
© A&C Black

Different modes: 1

- **Find the** │mode│ **for each set of data below and on Different modes: 2.**

The **mode** is the category that appears the most.

Tally chart to show pets owned by 6W

Pet	Tally
rabbit	IIII
dog	IIII IIII IIII
cat	IIII IIII IIII II
hamster	IIII IIII I
tortoise	I

Mode = _____

Bar chart to show favourite colours in 6W

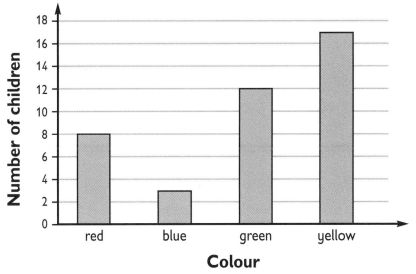

Mode = _____

Bar chart to show vehicles passing the playground

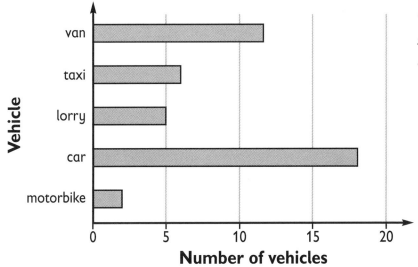

Mode = _____

Teachers' note Use in conjunction with 'Different modes: 2'. This activity consolidates the concept of the mode as an average. At the start of the lesson, ask the children to remind each other what the mode is and ask them to give examples for their class, for example the mode for the colour of socks is white.

A Lesson for Every Day
Maths
10–11 Years
© A&C Black

Different modes: 2

Pie chart to show favourite fruit in 6K

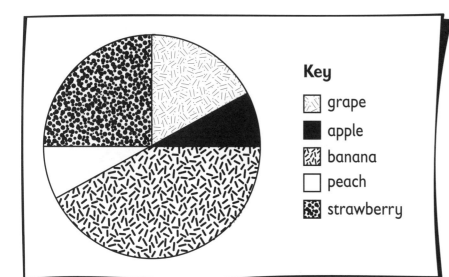

Key

⬦ grape

■ apple

▨ banana

☐ peach

▦ strawberry

Mode = _____

Birds seen on a nature walk

We saw these birds:
robin, blackbird, thrush, robin, crow,
sparrow, blackbird, robin, sparrow,
sparrow, crow, sparrow, blackbird

Mode = _____

Table of test scores

Name	Test score
Amy	4
Ben	5
Ella	5
Callam	7
Eddie	9
Alia	6
George	3
Deepak	4
Isabel	6
James	5
Chloe	10

Mode = _____

Teachers' note Use in conjunction with 'Different modes: 1'.

A Lesson for Every Day
Maths
10–11 Years
© A&C Black

Paul's pool party

- **Paul invited his friends to his birthday pool party.**
- **Find the** mean **of each set of data about the swimming pool.**

The mean is the sum of all the data divided by the number of pieces of data.

Water toys in the pool			
Floats: 12	Balls: 25	Giant inflatable animals: 1	Inflatable rings: 14

1 The mean number of water toys is _____ .

Ages of people at the party														
5	7	7	8	10	10	10	10	10	10	10	10	11	11	21

2 The mean age of people at the party is _____ .

Temperature of children's pool in °C				
8 am: 25·5 °C	9 am: 25·7 °C	10 am: 26·2 °C	11 am: 26·6 °C	12 noon: 26 °C

3 The mean temperature of the pool is _____ °C.

Number of children in swimming lessons with Mr Splash				
Mon: 12	Tues: 5	Wed: 10	Thurs: 20	Fri: 8

4 The mean number of children in a swimming lesson is _____ .

Number of people in the pools in the morning		
Main pool: 35	Children's pool: 11	Splash pool: 2

5 The mean number of people in the pools is _____ .

- **Do you think that the mean for this data is helpful?**

Discuss your ideas with a partner.

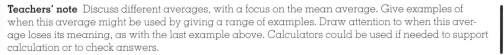

Teachers' note Discuss different averages, with a focus on the mean average. Give examples of when this average might be used by giving a range of examples. Draw attention to when this average loses its meaning, as with the last example above. Calculators could be used if needed to support calculation or to check answers.

A Lesson for Every Day
Maths
10–11 Years
© A&C Black

In the middle: 1

Craig asked his friends some questions.
The data he collected is shown below and on
In the middle: 2.

- Find the [median] for each set of data.
  To do this, write the data in order and
  then draw a ring around the middle value.

> The **median** is the middle value once a set of data has been ordered.

• **What size feet do you have?**

5, 3, 4, 5, 3·5, 4, 4·5, 4·5, 5, 5·5, 5, 4, 3·5

• **How old are you in years and months?**

10y 2m, 10y 5m, 10y 4m, 10y 2m, 10y 3m, 10y 4m, 10y 6m,
10y 3m, 10y 5m

NOW TRY THIS!

- **On the back of this sheet, write seven numbers from 0 to 100. Make 43 the median.**

Teachers' note Use in conjunction with 'In the middle: 2'. Give examples of when the median is useful. The children could collect data from others in the class, linked to the questions above, and use it to find the range, median, mode and mean.

A Lesson for Every Day
Maths
10-11 Years
© A&C Black

In the middle: 2

- Find the median for each set of data below, by putting the data in order and then drawing a ring around the middle value.

- **How many brothers and sisters do you have?**

0, 1, 3, 2, 1, 0, 1, 1, 3, 2, 1, 2, 1, 0, 4

- **What is your favourite number between 1 and 20?**

14, 2, 4, 11, 19, 2, 18, 16, 15, 13, 12, 2, 17, 8, 3, 9, 5

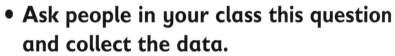

NOW TRY THIS!

- **Choose one of Craig's questions.**
- **Ask people in your class this question and collect the data.**
- **Find the median for your data.**

Teachers' note Use in conjunction with 'In the middle: 1'.

A Lesson for Every Day
Maths
10–11 Years
© A&C Black

105

Weather station

- **What data could you collect about the weather?**
- **Talk to a partner about some investigations you could carry out and record your ideas below.**

- **Choose one investigation.**
- **How will you collect and record the data?**

_____

_____

_____

_____

Think!
Will you be able to
collect the data
all in one go?
Or will you have to take
measurements every
day for a week, or
every hour in a day?

- **On paper or using ICT, design a recording sheet.**
- **What do you predict the data will tell you?** _____

_____

_____

Teachers' note Discuss ideas about how to collect data. If possible, make simple recording instruments to measure rainfall. The children will need plain, squared or lined paper for their recording sheets. Alternatively, these could be designed using ICT and presented on an interactive whiteboard for discussion and evaluation.

A Lesson for Every Day
Maths
10–11 Years
© A&C Black

Salad bar

The number of salad portions served in a café was recorded for one week.

		Monday	Tuesday	Wednesday	Thursday	Friday	Frequency for week
Grated carrot		‖‖ ‖‖ ‖	‖‖ ‖‖	‖‖ ‖‖ ‖‖	‖‖ ‖‖ ‖‖	‖‖ ‖‖	57
Sweetcorn		‖‖ ‖	‖‖‖‖	‖‖‖‖	‖‖	‖‖ ‖	
Lettuce		‖‖ ‖‖‖‖	‖‖ ‖‖ ‖	‖‖ ‖‖‖‖	‖‖ ‖	‖‖ ‖‖	
Beetroot		‖‖ ‖	‖‖ ‖	‖‖ ‖‖ ‖	‖‖ ‖‖ ‖	‖‖ ‖‖ ‖	
Mixed pepper		‖‖ ‖‖ ‖‖‖‖	‖‖ ‖‖ ‖‖	‖‖ ‖‖ ‖	‖‖ ‖‖ ‖‖	‖‖ ‖‖ ‖‖	
Cucumber		‖‖ ‖‖ ‖‖‖‖	‖‖ ‖‖‖‖	‖‖ ‖‖	‖‖ ‖‖	‖‖ ‖‖‖‖	

- **Complete the frequency table and answer these questions.**

1 What was the most popular salad choice overall? _____

2 How many portions of beetroot were served in total? _____

3 What was the **least** popular choice on Monday? _____

4 On which day were 12 portions of lettuce served? _____

5 Five portions of a salad choice were served on one day.
   a What was the salad choice? _____
   b On which day was it served? _____

6 Who do you think this data is useful for?

Discuss your ideas with a partner.

NOW TRY THIS!

60 portions of salad were served on Friday.

- **Do you agree with this statement?** _____
- **Explain your answer to your partner.**

Teachers' note Discuss the layout of the frequency chart to ensure that the children understand what each cell represents. As a further extension, the children could draw bar charts to represent the data.

A Lesson for Every Day
Maths
10-11 Years
© A&C Black

Stretchy statistics: 1

Class 6S measured how far three springs stretched when different weights were added. Here are the results for Spring B.

Weight added	0 g	100 g	200 g	300 g	400 g	500 g	600 g	700 g	800 g
Length of spring	8·5 cm	9 cm	9·5 cm	10 cm	10·5 cm	11 cm	11·5 cm	12 cm	12·5 cm

- **Plot the data for Spring B as a line graph.**

Use the line graph on Stretchy statistics: 2.

1 What was the length of spring B before any weights were added? _____ cm

2 How many centimetres long was spring B when 800 g were added? _____ cm

3 What would be the approximate length of spring B when 250 g were added? _____ cm

NOW TRY THIS!

- **Which spring stretched the furthest?** ___

Weight added	Length of spring		
	A	B	C
0 g	8 cm	8·5 cm	9 cm
800 g	10 cm	12·5 cm	12·5 cm

Teachers' note Use in conjunction with 'Stretchy statistics: 2'. This activity could be linked to the class carrying out the investigation in a science lesson. Data generated from weights added to elastic bands or springs could be plotted, compared and discussed. Simple conclusions could be made and further lines of enquiry suggested.

A Lesson for Every Day
Maths
10–11 Years
© A&C Black

Stretchy statistics: 2

Line graph to show the length of spring B

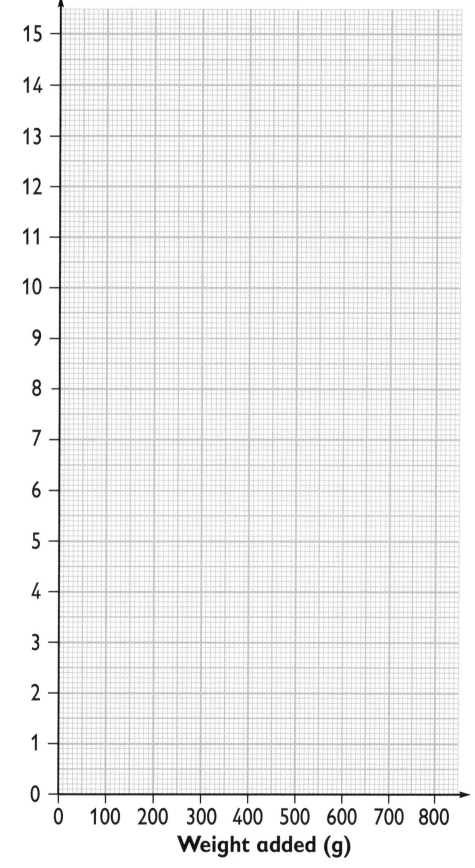

Teachers' note Use in conjunction with 'Stretchy statistics: 1'.

A Lesson for Every Day
Maths
10-11 Years
© **A&C Black**

109

Plant sale: 1

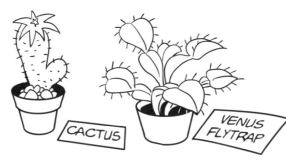

The pie charts on Plant sale: 2 show the sales of plants each week for a month.

• **Use the pie charts to answer these questions.**

1 In week 1:

   a How many cacti were sold? _____

   b How many spider plants were sold? _____

2 In week 2, four orchids were sold.
   What was the total number of plants sold during that week? _____

3 In week 3, twenty-four Venus flytraps were sold.
   How many plants were sold in total during that week? _____

4 In week 4, how many more orchids than cacti were sold? _____

5 In which week were the most plants sold? _____

6 In which weeks were twelve orchids sold? _____

7 In which week were eight Venus flytraps sold? _____

8 How many spider plants were sold in total during the four weeks? _____

NOW TRY THIS!

• **The shop decides to sell only three types of plant. Which plant do you think they should stop selling, and why do you think this?** _____

_____

Teachers' note Use in conjunction with 'Plant sale: 2'. Discuss how a pie chart is constructed and how the concept of proportion refers to parts of a whole, rather than specific numbers or values. Draw attention to the number of sectors into which the pie charts are divided and revise how concepts of division will help the children to answer the questions.

A Lesson for Every Day
Maths
10–11 Years
© A&C Black

Plant sale: 2

Key

 Venus flytrap   cactus   spider plant   ☐ orchid

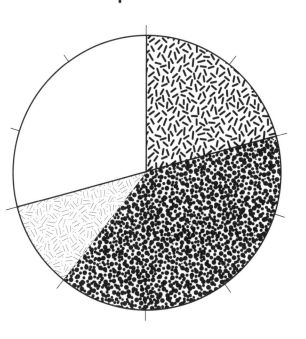

Week 1: 40 plants sold in total

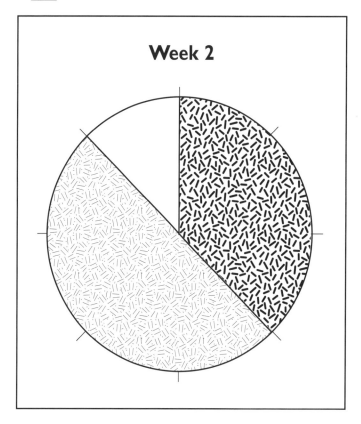

Week 2

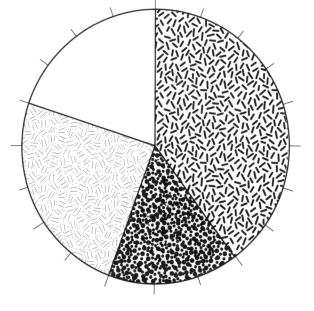

Week 3

Week 4: 36 plants sold in total

Teachers' note Use in conjunction with 'Plant sale: 1'.

A Lesson for Every Day
Maths
10–11 Years
© A&C Black

Side orders

These side orders were taken at Cath's Café.

	Mon	Tues	Wed	Thurs	Fri	Sat	Sun
Onion rings	4	9	3	0	3	7	11
Garlic bread	5	8	2	7	5	7	4
Chips	12	17	7	16	12	11	15
Green salad	8	6	4	7	7	10	14
Mixed peppers	9	11	3	11	8	16	15

● **Calculate the range, mean, median and mode for each food item.**

	Range	Mean	Median	Mode
Onion rings				
Garlic bread				
Chips				
Green salad				
Mixed peppers				

1 Which food item has a median of 7? _____

2 Which food item has a mode of 11? _____

3 Which food item has a mean of 8? _____

4 a Which food item should Cath definitely serve? _____

　b Why do you think so? _____

_____

5 a Which food item could Cath stop serving? _____

　b Why do you think so? _____

_____

Teachers' note Ask the children to give simple definitions of the range, mean, median and mode before starting this activity. Talk about the layout of the data and discuss how the average for each item can be calculated across the week, or for each day. The children can use a calculator to find the mean averages. If necessary, revise how to record to one decimal place.

A Lesson for Every Day
Maths
10–11 Years
© A&C Black

Best average

- **Calculate the mean, median and mode for each set of data.**
- **Ring the average that you think is the best, and explain why.**

---

1 Computer game scores

58 38 47 44 38

mean ☐   median ☐   mode ☐

Explanation: _____

_____

_____

_____

---

2 Number of pets owned
2, 3, 1, 0, 5, 1, 4, 11, 2, 3, 1

mean ☐   median ☐   mode ☐

Explanation: _____

_____

_____

_____

---

3 Shoe sizes
2, 5, 3, 4, 3, 5, 4, 6, 5, 5, 3, 4, 5

mean ☐   median ☐   mode ☐

Explanation: _____

_____

_____

_____

NOW TRY THIS!

Here are Sophie's scores in the weekly spelling test: 5, 7, 5, 6, 8

- **Which average do you think she would give as her average score?**

Explain your choice to a partner.

Teachers' note In this activity, the children calculate each average for the same set of data. The focus is on evaluating which average is the best one to use in each situation. The children could discuss this in pairs. Question 3 involves a decimal average: provide calculators, if necessary, and remind the children how to record to one decimal place.

A Lesson for Every Day
Maths
10–11 Years
© A&C Black

Cube collection

How many cubes do you think you can pick up in one hand?

Work in a group of five.

- **In your group, take three turns each.**
- **Record the results in this table.**

You need a copy of this worksheet each....

...and some cubes.

Name	1st turn	2nd turn	3rd turn

1 a Which average will you use for your score? _____

  b Why would you choose this average? _____

  _____

2 Calculate the median, mean and mode for your scores.

  median ____   mean ____   mode ____

3 a What is the median, mean and mode for your group?

  median ____   mean ____   mode ____

  b How do these compare with other groups' averages?

4 Which is the fairest 'average' to use?

Discuss your ideas with your group.

NOW TRY THIS!

Hanif picked up these numbers of cubes: 8, 7, 9.

The median and the mean are the same.

- **Do you agree with his statement?**
- **Explain your answer to a partner.**

Teachers' note Each group will need interlocking cubes (or other cubes all of the same size). The children should consider which average they might want to use, as well as thinking about which average is most representative of their results. Calculators could be made available for calculating the averages for the group data.

A Lesson for Every Day
Maths
10–11 Years
© A&C Black

Chess guess: 1

You need Chess guess: 2.

There are 32 pieces in a chess set.
Sam puts all the pieces into a cloth bag
and picks one out without looking.

1 Which of the following chess pieces is she **more likely** to pick?

Underline the piece that you think I am **more likely** to pick.
If you think it is **equally likely**, underline both pieces.

a a knight or a queen?

c a pawn or a black piece?

e a knight or a rook?

b a rook or a white piece?

d a black piece or a bishop?

f a white king or a black rook?

2 Complete these statements.

a Sam is less likely to pick a _____ than a _____.

b Sam is more likely to pick a _____ than a _____.

c Sam is equally likely to pick a _____ as a _____.

3 a Which type of chess piece is she **most likely** to pick? _____

b Why do you think so? _____

_____

NOW TRY THIS!

Sam is more likely to pick a queen than a king.

That's wrong!

- **Talk to a partner about who you think is right**
and explain your reasoning.

Teachers' note Use in conjunction with 'Chess guess: 2'. No prior knowledge of chess is needed, though it would be useful to have available a chess set so that the children can see and discuss the data for this activity. (Note: some children might know a 'rook' as a 'castle'.) The children can use the chess pieces as data for other questions and statements to discuss in pairs.

A Lesson for Every Day
Maths
10-11 Years
© A&C Black

Chess guess: 2

rook   knight   bishop   queen   king   bishop   knight   rook

pawn   pawn   pawn   pawn   pawn   pawn   pawn   pawn

rook   knight   bishop   queen   king   bishop   knight   rook

pawn   pawn   pawn   pawn   pawn   pawn   pawn   pawn

Teachers' note Use in conjunction with 'Chess guess: 1'.

A Lesson for Every Day
Maths
10–11 Years
© A&C Black

Chance landing

A
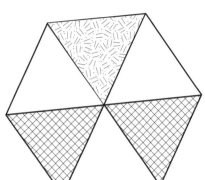

B
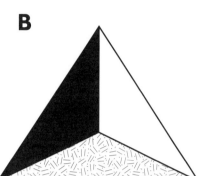

C
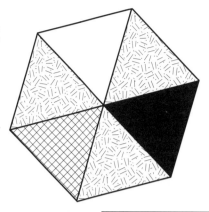

D
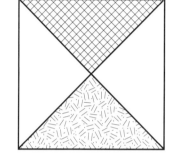

1 Which spinner is most likely to land on ▨ ? ___

2 Which spinner is least likely to land on ▨ ? ___

3 Tick **true** or **false** for each statement.

   a C is more likely to land on ▨ than on ☐ .   True ☐   False ☐

   b D is more likely to land on ▨ than on ▨ .   True ☐   False ☐

   c B is more likely to land on ▨ than on ■ .   True ☐   False ☐

4 How likely is it that each spinner will land on ☐ ?

   Choose from: impossible, unlikely, a fifty-fifty chance, likely, certain.

   A _____   B _____

   C _____   D _____

5 Complete the statements.

   Choose from: impossible, unlikely, a fifty-fifty chance, likely, certain.

   It is ___*unlikely*___ that spinner _A_ will land on ▨ .

   It is _____ that spinner ___ will land on ■ .

   It is _____ that spinner ___ will land on ▨ .

NOW TRY THIS!

- **Which is more likely: that spinner C will land on ▨ or that spinner D will land on ☐ ?**
- **Explain your thinking to a partner.**

Teachers' note The children could make spinners and experiment with their own shading and colouring. From this they could write their own statements and challenge others with questions about the spinners.

A Lesson for Every Day
Maths
10–11 Years
© A&C Black

Can you do better?

- **Choose a more suitable unit to measure the things below.**
- **Convert the measurement to that unit.**

1. Length of a shoe

0·25 m = _____25 cm_____

2. Height of a door

2000 mm = _____

3. Capacity of an eggcup

0·05 l = _____

4. Capacity of a bath

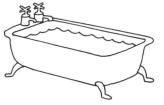

600 000 ml = _____

5. Mass of a car

1 500 000 g = _____

6. Distance from Bristol to Hull

367 000 m = _____

7. Length of the Great Wall of China

3 460 000 m = _____

8. Mass of a cricket ball

0·18 kg = _____

9. Height of a netball post

3000 mm = _____

10. Mass of a pen

0·01 kg = _____

11. Height of a house

0·01 km = _____

12. Circumference of the Earth

40 000 000 m = _____

13. Capacity of a bucket

8500 ml = _____

14. Length of a football pitch

9950 cm = _____

15. Length of a pencil sharpener

0·03 m = _____

Teachers' note Remind the children of the relationships between the standard metric units of measurement. As an extension activity, ask the children to write some measurements of their own in different ways and to say which is the most suitable to use. More confident children could explore imperial units such as inches, pints or miles.

A Lesson for Every Day
Maths
10–11 Years
© A&C Black

In the science lab

- **Read the scales and write the weight in grams.**
- **Write the letters in order from heaviest to lightest.**

A

0   1 kg

B

400 g   500 g

C
500 g   0   100 g

D
0   2 kg   4 kg

E
400 g   500 g   600 g

F
300 g   200 g   400 g   100 g   500 g   0

G
0·5   0·25   0·75   kg 0

H
0   500 g   1 kg

A _____   B _____   C _____   D _____

E _____   F _____   G _____   H _____

Heaviest _____ **Lightest**

Teachers' note Demonstrate how to count the number of intervals between two numbered positions and to divide the difference between the two numbers by the number of intervals: there are 10 intervals between 0 and 500 g, thus 500 g – 0 = 500 g and 500 g ÷ 10 = 50 g so each interval has a value of 50 g. As an extension activity, mark with an arrow the reading 425 g on every scale.

A Lesson for Every Day
Maths
10–11 Years
© A&C Black

In conclusion: 1

You need the worksheets called In conclusion: 2, 3 and 4.

Work with a partner.

- **Use the charts and graphs to help you answer the questions on each worksheet.**

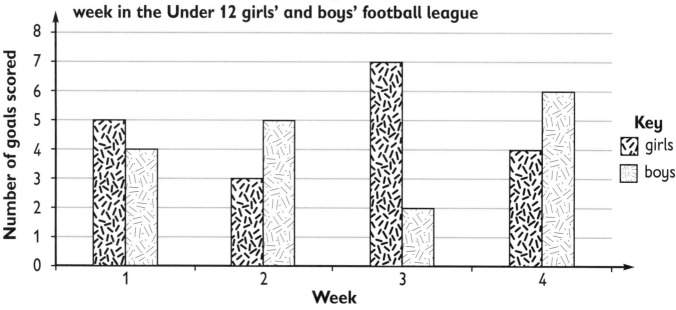

Bar chart to show the number of goals scored each week in the Under 12 girls' and boys' football league

Number of goals scored (y-axis: 0–8)

Week (x-axis: 1, 2, 3, 4)

Key
- girls
- boys

1 How many goals did the girls score in week 2? _____

2 How many goals did the boys score altogether? _____

Girls are better at football than boys.

3 a Based on the results, do you think that this statement is true? _____

b Explain your answer. _____

_____

_____

c What further data could you collect to check your answer?

_____

_____

Teachers' note Use in conjunction with 'In conclusion: 2, 3 and 4'. Discuss the term 'in conclusion' and the limitations of data. What does/doesn't the data tell you? What conclusions can be drawn? What further information should be gathered? Should we use experience to inform ideas, even if the data suggests otherwise?

120

A Lesson for Every Day
Maths
10–11 Years
© A&C Black

**A school carried out a sponsored sports challenge.
They raised £288.**

Pie chart to show the money raised by each class

Key
- ☐ Class 1
- ▦ Class 2
- ▨ Class 3
- ▤ Class 4
- ■ Class 5
- ▨ Class 6

1 Which classes each raised £24? _____

2 How much money did Class 3 raise? _____

3 'Class 4 is the best at sport.' What do you think about this statement?
Record your ideas below.

4 a 'Class 4 care the most about charity.'
Do you think the results show this statement to be true? _____

b Why do you think Class 4 raised the most money? _____

_____

_____

Teachers' note Use in conjunction with 'In conclusion: 1, 3 and 4'. Discuss the pie chart and how it shows data. Check the children understand that the larger the fraction that is shaded, the more money was raised. Ask them to say roughly what fraction of the £288 was raised by each class, and ask for suggestions as to how to work out how much this is.

A Lesson for Every Day
Maths
10–11 Years
© A&C Black

You need the worksheet called In conclusion: 4.

• **Look at the line graphs and bar charts.**

1 In which months was it hottest in London?

_____

2 What was the lowest temperature recorded in Rome? _____ °C

3 In which month was there 50 mm of rain in London? _____

4 How much rain fell in Rome in January? _____ mm

5 a 'Rome gets more rain than London'.
　　Based on the results, do you think this statement is true? _____

　b Explain your answer. _____

　　_____

　　_____

6 a 'The hotter it is, the dryer it is.' Do you agree with this? _____
　b Is this true for London and Rome? _____
　c Explain your answer. _____

　　_____

　　_____

7 On the back of this sheet, write two questions about the data for a partner to answer.

It is difficult to draw conclusions from some sets of data.

• **Do you agree with this statement?** _____
• **Talk to a partner about your ideas.**

Teachers' note Use in conjunction with 'In conclusion: 1, 2 amd 4'.

A Lesson for Every Day
Maths
10–11 Years
© A&C Black

In conclusion: 4

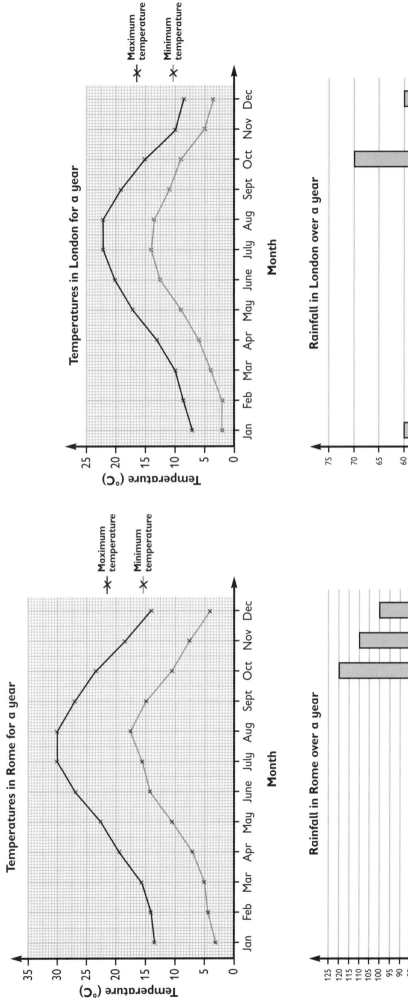

Temperatures in Rome for a year

Temperatures in London for a year

Rainfall in Rome over a year

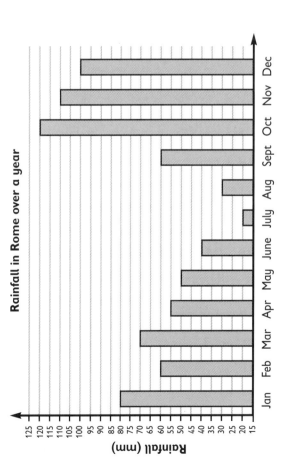

Rainfall in London over a year

Teachers' note Use in conjunction with 'In conclusion: 1, 2 and 3'.

A Lesson for Every Day
Maths
10–11 Years
© A&C Black

Miles to kilometres

- **Milly drew a** | conversion graph | **for miles and kilometres.**

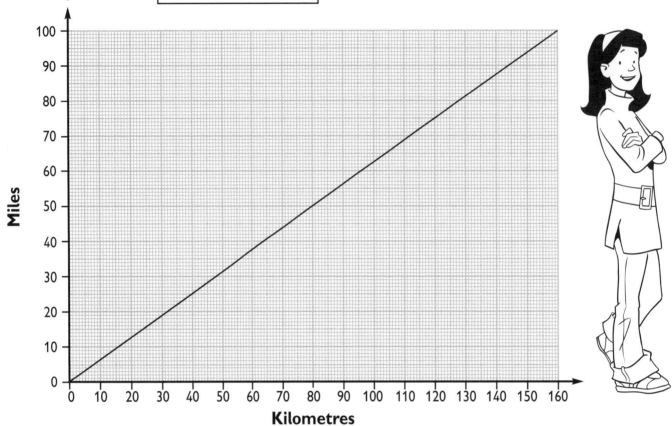

y-axis: Miles (0 to 100), x-axis: Kilometres (0 to 160)

- **Use the graph to complete these statements.**

1 a 50 miles = _____ km

  b 100 miles = _____ km

  c 10 miles = _____ km

  d 62 miles = _____ km

  e 35 miles = _____ km

2 a 40 km = _____ miles

  b 120 km = _____ miles

  c 95 km = _____ miles

  d 5 km = _____ miles

  e 150 km = _____ miles

- **Use the statements above to work out these conversions.**

3 a 1 mile = _____ km   **b** 1 km = _____ miles

NOW TRY THIS!

- **On the back of this sheet, explain how knowing that 100 miles = 160 km can help you to calculate what 2 miles is equivalent to.**

Teachers' note Talk about why the graph is a straight line and explain that the values are approximations only. Discuss the use of conversion graphs for other contexts, such as money and temperature.

A Lesson for Every Day
Maths
10-11 Years
© A&C Black

Per 100 grams

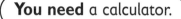

You need a calculator.

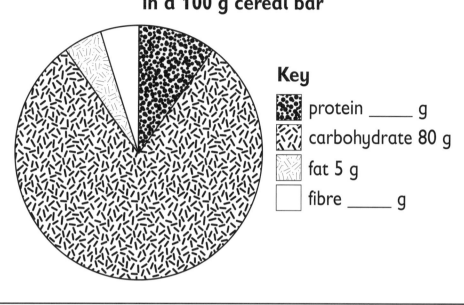

Pie chart to show the proportion of nutrients in a 100 g cereal bar

Key

- protein _____ g
- carbohydrate 80 g
- fat 5 g
- fibre _____ g

- ● **Use the pie chart to answer these questions.**

1 How many grams of fibre are there in the 100 g bar? Write this in the key.

2 How many grams of protein are there in the 100 g bar? Write this in the key.

3 Complete this table for cereal bars of different masses.

The proportion of nutrients for all the bars is the same as that of the 100 g bar.

Mass of bar	Protein	Carbohydrate	Fat	Fibre
200 g				
50 g				
120 g				
175 g				

NOW TRY THIS!

- ● **As a fraction, what proportion of fibre is in a cereal bar? _____**

Teachers' note Calculators should be available as the children work out how many grams would be in bars with different masses. During the plenary, discuss how the children used the pie chart to help them to work out the answers to questions 1 and 2, for example fibre is the same proportion as fat, so fibre is 5 g and protein is 10 g, since 100 g − 80 g − 5 g − 5 g = 10 g.

A Lesson for Every Day
Maths
10–11 Years
© A&C Black

Cheeky Chalky

Alice's dog, Chalky, has chewed her homework.

1 Fill in the missing numbers.

a 6, , 11, 14, 12, 8, 7, 9, 11, 4, 6   mode = 11

b 19, 31, 34, 83, 2, 13, 72, ⬜, 11   median = 31

c 5·6, 49·9, ⬜, 23·2, 64, 34·5, 22·7, 12·4   range = 80

d 24, 13, 7, ⬜, 39   mean = 20

e 4, 7, 13, 3, 11, 2, 5, ⬜, 15, 11, ⬜   mode = 7

f ⬜, 64, 8, 32, ⬜, 16, 2   median = 16

g 3, ⬜, 2, 4, 6, ⬜, 1   mean = 3

1 Which set of data has:
   a the largest range? ____   **b** the smallest range? ____

3 On the back of this sheet, write two questions about the data
   for a partner to answer.

NOW TRY THIS!

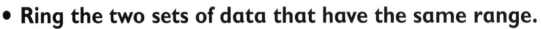

- **Ring the two sets of data that have the same range.**

   6, 2, 3, 7, 9, 1   3, 9, 6, 7, 12   2, 5, 14, 3, 7   16, 10, 8

Teachers' note Ensure that the children have a secure understanding of the range, mean, median and mode. Model how to find a missing answer. Calculators could be used to check answers. As a further extension, the children could make up their own data and ask others to find the missing value.

A Lesson for Every Day
Maths
10–11 Years
© **A&C Black**

Beijing 2008

These are the results of the Men's 100 metre sprint at the Beijing Olympics. The race took place on 16th August, 2008.

Surname of athlete	Country	Date of birth	Result
Thompson	Trinidad/Tobago	07.06.85	9.89 sec
Powell	Jamaica	23.11.82	9.95 sec
Burns	Trinidad/Tobago	07.01.83	10.01 sec
Bolt	Jamaica	21.08.86	9.69 sec
Martina	Netherland Antilles	03.07.84	9.93 sec
Patton	United States	04.12.77	10.03 sec
Frater	Jamaica	06.10.82	9.97 sec
Dix	United States	31.01.86	9.91 sec

1 Who won: **a** Gold? _____ **b** Silver? _____

   c Bronze? _____

2 How much faster was the athlete who
won gold than the athlete who won silver? _____ sec

3 What is the mean time (to two decimal places) of the athletes? _____ sec

4 What is the difference in time between the
athlete who won gold and the mean time? _____ sec

5 What is the median time? _____ sec

6 What was the age of:

   a the oldest athlete? _____ years _____ months

   b the youngest athlete? _____ years _____ months

7 What is the range of the athletes' ages? _____ years _____ months

NOW TRY THIS!

- **Which athlete's time was
nearest to the mean time?** _____

Teachers' note Discuss the data to ensure that the children understand the headings. Calculators should be made available for this activity. Extension work could include children asking further questions about the data and researching other data from the most recent Olympic Games.

A Lesson for Every Day
Maths
10-11 Years
© A&C Black

Shady business

- **Follow the instructions for each spinner.**

A

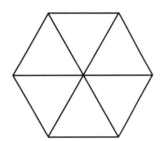

Shade the spinner so that it is **more likely** to land on ■ than on ▨ .

B

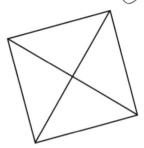

Shade the spinner so that it is **less likely** to land on ☐ than on ▨ .

C

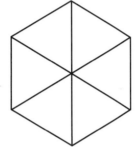

Shade the spinner so that it is **certain** to land on ▨ .

D

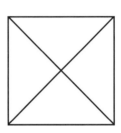

Colour the spinner so that it is **equally likely** to land on green as on red.

E

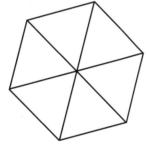

Colour the spinner so that it is **impossible** to land on red.

F

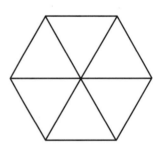

Colour the spinner so that it is **very likely** to land on blue.

G

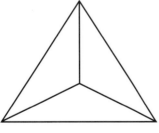

Colour the spinner so that it is **more likely** to land on green than on blue.

H

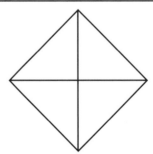

Colour the spinner so that it is **impossible** to land on green or white.

Teachers' note Colouring pencils are required for this activity.

A Lesson for Every Day
Maths
10–11 Years
© A&C Black

A dice landing on 6

A coin landing on 'heads' or 'tails'

A dice landing on an even number

Picking 'September' from a pack of 'months of the year' cards

Picking a white piece from a chess set

A dice landing on 3

Throwing a total of 12 with two dice

Throwing a total of 7 with two dice

A coin landing on 'heads'

Picking a pawn from a chess set

This spinner landing on the shaded part

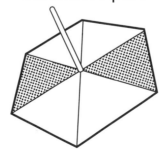

Picking a black piece from a chess set

Teachers' note Use in conjunction with 'More likely: 2'. The children play the game in pairs or small groups. Each pair/group will need one set of cards. (See page 15 for instructions on how to play the game.) The statements on the cards relate to something being picked at random from a whole set. Individuals or pairs could also order events from least likely to most likely.

A Lesson for Every Day
Maths
10–11 Years
© A&C Black

A coin landing on 'tails'

Picking a vowel from a pack of alphabet cards

A dice landing on an odd number

Picking a 7 from a pack of 0–9 digit cards

Picking a white king from a chess set

Picking a circle from these shapes

Picking a square from these shapes.

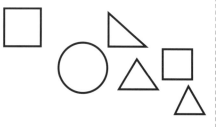

Throwing two dice and one landing on 3

Picking 'Tuesday' from a pack of 'days of the week' cards

This spinner landing on the shaded part

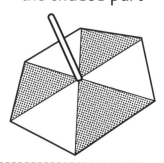

This spinner landing on the shaded part

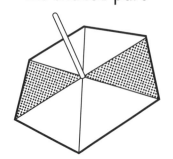

This spinner landing on the shaded part

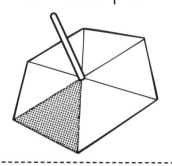

Teachers' note Use in conjunction with 'More likely: 1'. No prior knowledge of chess is needed, though it would be useful to have available a chess set so that the children can see and discuss the data for this activity.

A Lesson for Every Day
Maths
10–11 Years
© A&C Black

Measurement bingo

- **Choose any 12 bingo balls and write the measurements onto a blank bingo board. Your teacher will call out measurements that are equivalent to these.**

- **Can you be first to get three in a row?**

Game 1

Game 2

Game 3

1·2 m	300 g	5·5 km	2500 ml	3·7 l	0·9 cm	1·24 kg
55 mm	250 g	3 kg	370 ml	0·09 m	78 cm	2·8 l
4000 ml	750 g	450 mm	0·4 m	3700 m	150 cm	2730 m
0·7 kg	3·25 m	680 g	0·22 kg	5 km	0·2 cm	11·9 cm

Teachers' note When measurements have been written onto one game board, call out measurements that are equivalent to those on the balls, for example for 150 cm call out 1.5 m or 1500 mm. A list of possible measurements to call out is given on page 15. Measurements can be altered before copying to make them easier or harder as appropriate.

A Lesson for Every Day
Maths
10-11 Years
© A&C Black

Arrow error

Some of these scales show the correct reading and some don't.

- Tick which are correct and draw a new arrow on those that
  are wrong.

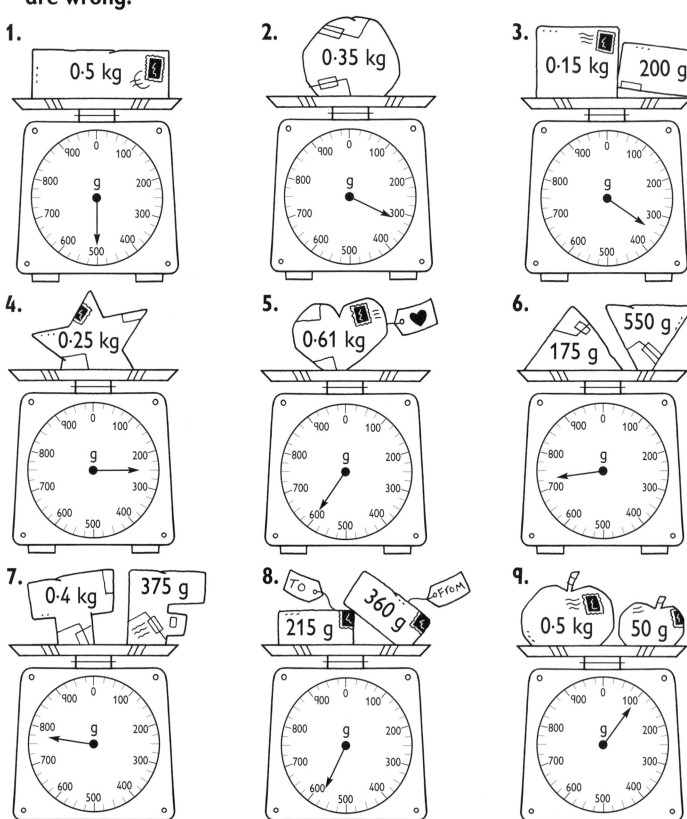

1. 0·5 kg

2. 0·35 kg

3. 0·15 kg   200 g

4. 0·25 kg

5. 0·61 kg

6. 550 g   175 g

7. 0·4 kg   375 g

8. TO   360 g   FROM   215 g

9. 0·5 kg   50 g

Teachers' note Encourage the children to read the scales as accurately as they can. The arrows and masses could be adjusted before copying to provide a range of different scales to read and to provide differentiation. As an extension activity, ask the children to write each reading on the scales in kilograms.

A Lesson for Every Day
Maths
10–11 Years
© A&C Black

Patrick's patterns

Patrick has been making patterns with rectangles and squares of these sizes:

4 cm [7 cm rectangle] 5 cm [5 cm square]
7 cm   5 cm

• Find the height and width of each pattern.

Record your calculations on a separate piece of paper.

1
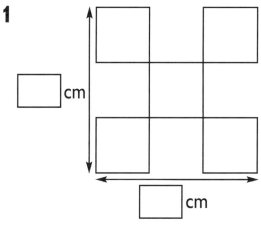

☐ cm

☐ cm

2
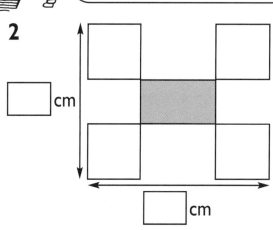

☐ cm

☐ cm

3
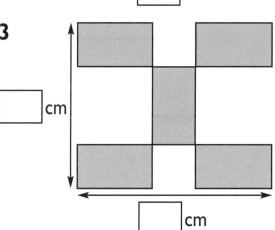

☐ cm

☐ cm

4
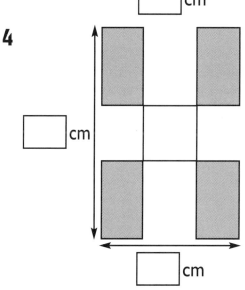

☐ cm

☐ cm

5
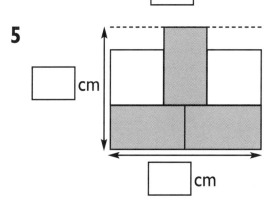

☐ cm

☐ cm

6
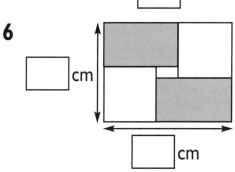

☐ cm

☐ cm

NOW TRY THIS!

• Talk to a partner about the calculations you did for each pattern.

Teachers' note 'Model thinking' can be used as an extension to this activity as it requires much greater visualisation skills, working in three, rather than two, dimensions. Focus on the discussion of how each problem was solved and ask the children to record the calculations used.

A Lesson for Every Day
Maths
10-11 Years
© A&C Black

Model thinking

Each building brick is identical in size.
The lengths of the sides are 7 cm, 2 cm and 4 cm.

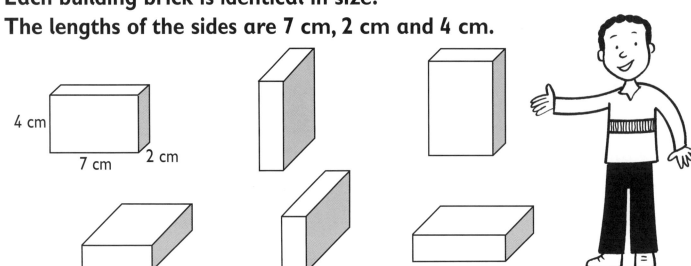

James makes some models with the bricks.

• **Work out the length shown by each dotted line.**

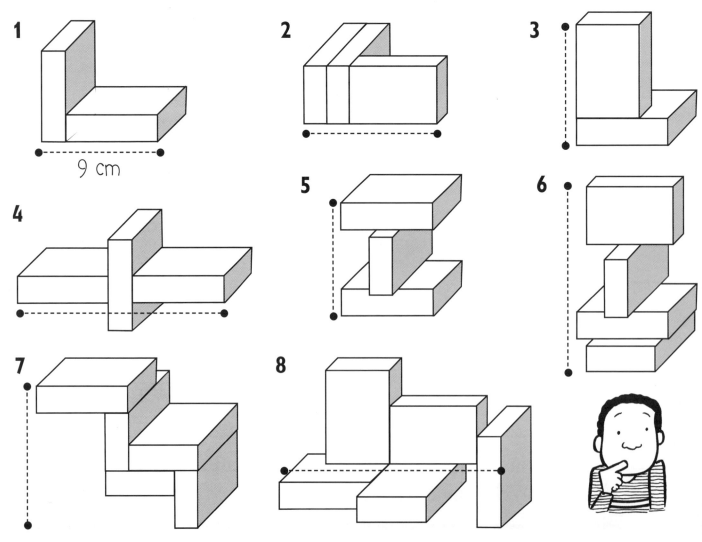

1

9 cm

2

3

4

5

6

7

8

Teachers' note Some children may find the visualisation of these models difficult and could be given similar-shaped bricks to use to construct the models. Encourage the children to discuss their reasoning with a partner and to compare their answers. If desired, the children could find the other dimensions of the models.

A Lesson for Every Day
Maths
10–11 Years
© A&C Black

Dragon trail

- Answer each question, writing any remainders as whole numbers.
- Colour the answers that have a remainder of 3 to form a trail to help the dragon escape from the princess.

43 ÷ 8 = 5 r3	39 ÷ 4 =	58 ÷ 5 =	48 ÷ 9 =
	31 ÷ 7 =	72 ÷ 5 =	41 ÷ 6 =
27 ÷ 6 =	28 ÷ 5 =	35 ÷ 4 =	51 ÷ 5 =
	35 ÷ 8 =	66 ÷ 9 =	45 ÷ 6 =
86 ÷ 5 =	38 ÷ 7 =	43 ÷ 4 =	67 ÷ 8 =
	28 ÷ 8 =	88 ÷ 9 =	52 ÷ 7 =
99 ÷ 5 =	82 ÷ 4 =	57 ÷ 9 =	57 ÷ 8 =
	59 ÷ 6 =	93 ÷ 5 =	55 ÷ 7 =
31 ÷ 8 =	62 ÷ 9 =	57 ÷ 6 =	83 ÷ 3 =
	91 ÷ 4 =	87 ÷ 7 =	94 ÷ 6 =
75 ÷ 8 =	76 ÷ 9 =	97 ÷ 4 =	97 ÷ 8 =
	99 ÷ 4 =	88 ÷ 5 =	80 ÷ 7 =
98 ÷ 3 =	85 ÷ 6 =	98 ÷ 8 =	99 ÷ 4 =

NOW TRY THIS!

- Write all the numbers between 50 and 100 that have a remainder of 2 when divided by 3.

Teachers' note Encourage the children to use mental methods of division to work out these divisions, such as partitioning the number into a multiple of the divisor and a bit, for example 47 ÷ 7 = (42 + 5) ÷ 7 = 42 ÷ 7 remainder 5 = 6 r5.

A Lesson for Every Day
Maths
10-11 Years
© A&C Black

Shopping parade

- ## Use written methods of multiplication to solve these problems.

1. 7 shops are joined as a terrace. Each shop is 3·27 m wide. What is the width of the terrace? ☐

2. The bicycle shop wants to display 4 bikes in a line. Each bike is 1·28 m long. How much space is needed? ☐

3. At the card shop, birthday cards cost £1.59. How much for 7 cards? ☐

4. At the greengrocers, a bag of apples weighs 1·25 kg. How much do 9 bags weigh? ☐

5. At the music store, a CD costs £11.79. How much for 4 CDs? ☐

6. Magazines from the newsagent cost £3.29. How much for 8 magazines? ☐

7. At the greengrocers, potatoes are £4 per kilogram. How much for 2·78 kg of potatoes? ☐

8. At the pet shop, cat treats cost £6 per kilogram. How much for 1·78 kg of cat treats? ☐

9. At the joke shop, hairy warts cost £3.72 per pack. How much for 7 packs? ☐

NOW TRY THIS!

- ## Find each answer in the code below and ring its corresponding letter.

A	S	T	B	E	R
26·32	42·22	10·68	25·59	11·12	22·89
P	**Z**	**M**	**L**	**I**	**U**
11·25	26·04	6·72	25·88	11·13	47·16

- ## Rearrange the ringed letters to spell out the name of a shape. _____

Teachers' note Provide the children with paper on which to show their written methods. Encourage them to make sensible estimates for each calculation before they carry it out and to use the estimate to check whether the final answer is a sensible one.

A Lesson for Every Day
Maths
10-11 Years
© A&C Black

Best estimate

- ## Tick which contestant has given the most sensible estimate.

SADIE   CHARLIE   ELLIE

	Sadie	Charlie	Ellie
1. Estimate the length of a tennis court.	250 m	25 m	250 cm
2. Estimate the mass of a 1p coin.	1 g	20 g	50 g
3. Estimate the capacity of a kettle.	2 l	50 ml	200 ml
4. Estimate the area of this worksheet.	60 cm^2	600 cm^2	6000 cm^2
5. Estimate the diameter of a football.	0·7 m	50 cm	300 mm
6. Estimate the area of a whiteboard.	40 cm^2	4 m^2	0.4 m^2
7. Estimate the perimeter of an exercise book cover.	0·08 m	8 m	80 cm
8. Estimate the mass of a box of matches.	30 g	800 g	0·7 g
9. Estimate the distance from Glasgow to Manchester.	35 km	350 km	3500 km

NOW TRY THIS!

- ## Make up an estimation game for your partner.
  ☆ On cards, write things that can be measured.
  ☆ On the back of the card, write three estimates for each.
  ☆ Ask your partner to say which is the best estimate.

Teachers' note These estimates could be altered before copying if desired.

A Lesson for Every Day
Maths
10-11 Years
© A&C Black

Measure up: 1

- **Read the amount of liquid in the three test tubes. All the liquid is poured into the large container.**
- **Draw the liquid to the correct level.**

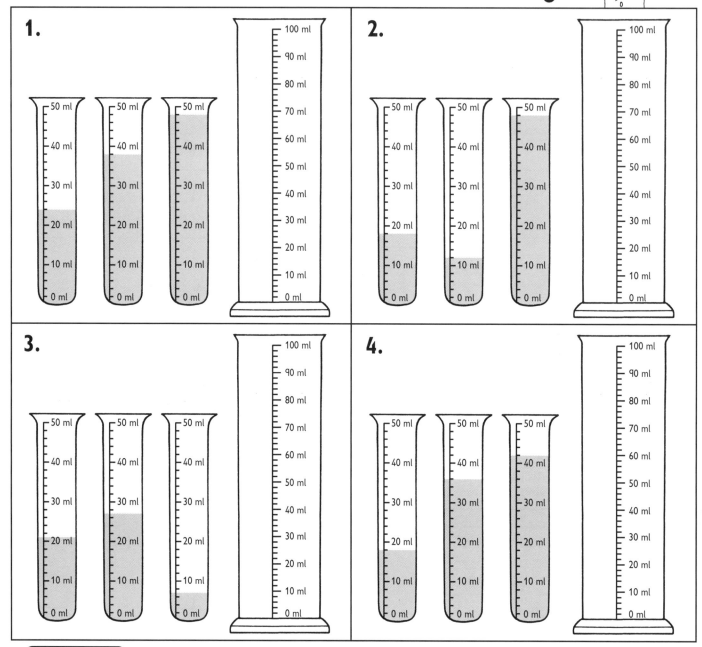

Your teacher will give you a new sheet.

- **Make up six questions for a partner to solve.**
- **Make sure that there is never a total of more than 100 ml in the three test tubes.**

Teachers' note For the extension activity, provide the children with 'Measure up: 2'. Some children might benefit from the sheet being enlarged. The numbers on the sheet could be altered to provide more differentiation, for example by going up in steps of 5 ml so that each mark represents 1 ml or by going up in 50s or 100s, where each mark represents 10 ml or 20 ml.

A Lesson for Every Day
Maths
10–11 Years
© A&C Black

Measure up: 2

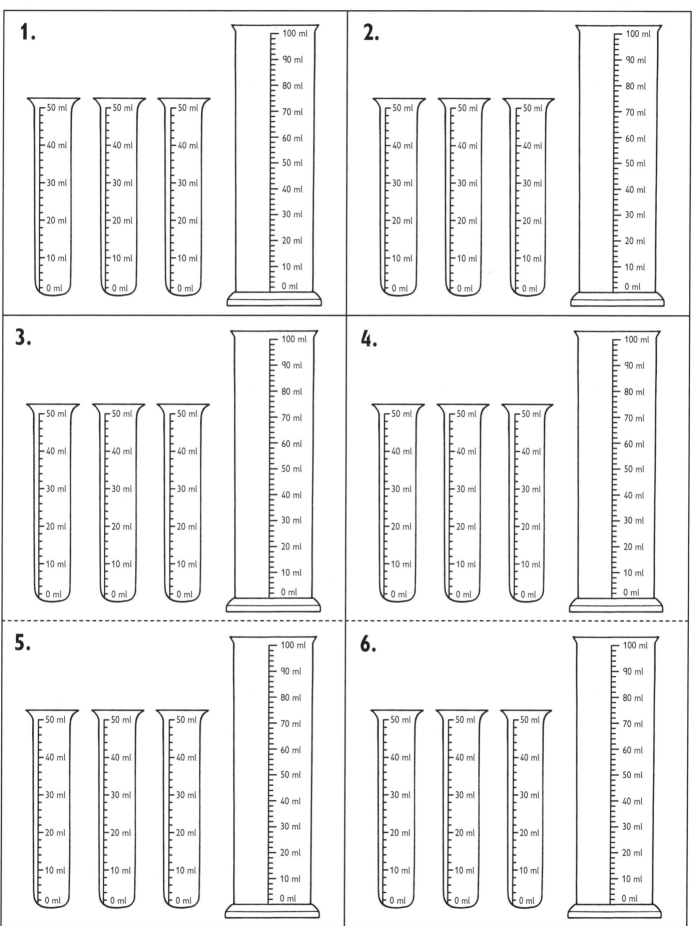

1.

2.

3.

4.

5.

6.

Teachers' note Use in conjunction with 'Measure up: 1'. Some children might benefit from the sheet being enlarged. The numbers on the scales could be altered to provide more differentiation, for example by going up in steps of 5 ml so that each mark represents 1 ml or by going up in 50s or 100s, where each mark represents 10 ml or 20 ml.

A Lesson for Every Day
Maths
10–11 Years
© A&C Black

Perimeter patterns

Each pattern has been made with identical triangular tiles, like this one.

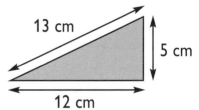

* Work out the perimeter of each pattern.

NOW TRY THIS!

* Sketch patterns that could be made using this tile.
* Write the perimeter of each pattern.

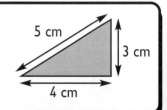

Teachers' note Demonstrate how to use subtraction to find the length remaining when a 5 cm side is placed along a 12 cm or 13 cm side. The children could also be told that the area of each tile is 30 cm² and the area of each pattern could be found.

A Lesson for Every Day
Maths
10-11 Years
© A&C Black

Rectangular reasoning

- **For each shape below, write the lengths of the bold unmarked sides, using the other measurements given.**
- **Find the** [ ] **of each shape.**

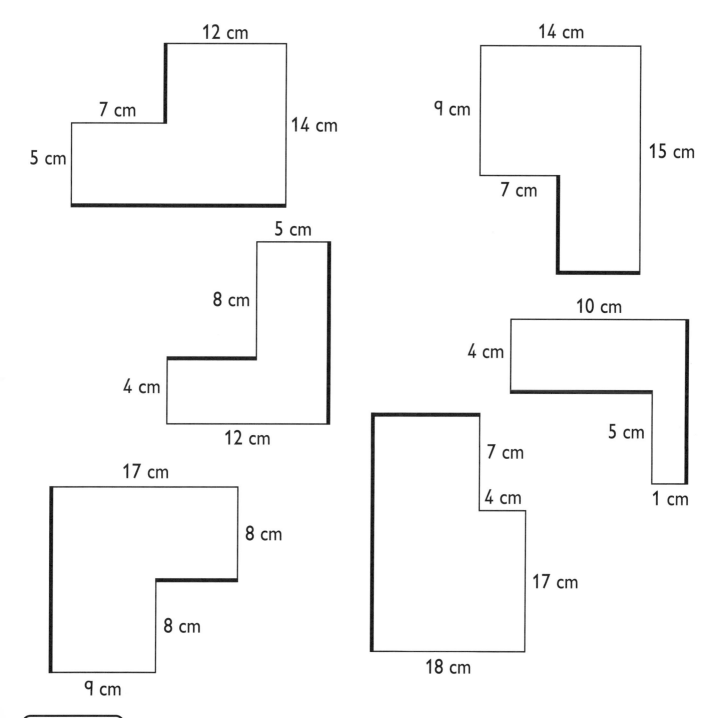

12 cm

7 cm

14 cm

5 cm

14 cm

9 cm

15 cm

7 cm

5 cm

8 cm

4 cm

12 cm

10 cm

4 cm

5 cm

1 cm

7 cm

4 cm

17 cm

18 cm

17 cm

8 cm

8 cm

9 cm

NOW TRY THIS!

- **Make up one of your own for a partner to solve.**

Teachers' note This sheet can be used for area or perimeter or for both. Write 'perimeter', 'area' or 'perimeter and area' into the box. If the children are finding the area, demonstrate how to split the shape up into rectangles (note that there is generally more than one way that this can be done) and to find the areas of the rectangles and then the total area.

A Lesson for Every Day
Maths
10-11 Years
© A&C Black

141

Rocky's wall and rockery

I am moving a pile of stones to different parts of my garden.
I fill my barrow, wheel it 12 m, and take out the large stones for a wall.
I wheel the rest of the stones 9 m and leave them for a rockery.
I return to the pile for more stones. In total, I make 20 trips.

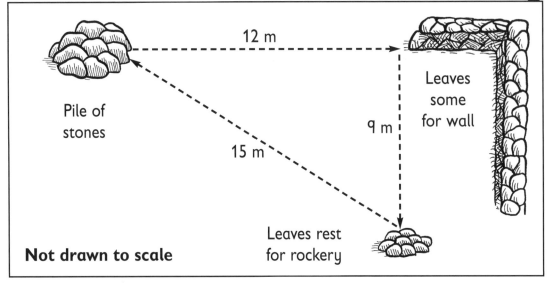

1 How far does Rocky push the barrow in total? _____ m

2 For what fraction of this distance is his barrow:
  a full? _____   **b** partly full? _____   **c** empty? _____

3 On each trip, Rocky puts 50 kg of stones in his barrow.
  What mass of stones has he moved after the 20 trips? _____ kg

4 On average, Rocky leaves 18 kg of large stones for his wall on
  each trip. What is the total weight of the stones for the wall? _____ kg

I need to buy cement and sand for my wall.

5 For each 60 kg of large stones, Rocky needs 25 kg of
  cement. How much cement does he need to buy? _____ kg

6 Cement comes in 50-kg bags and costs £8.50 per bag.
  How much will Rocky spend on cement? £ _____

7 Rocky needs to buy sand at a ratio of 3 parts sand to 1 part cement.
  How many kilograms of sand will he need? _____ kg

8 A 25-kg bag of sand costs £1.90? Altogether,
  how much will Rocky spend on sand and cement? £ _____

Teachers' note As an extension, ask the children to make up further related questions in this context
for a partner to solve, for example considering the mass of the stones not used for the wall, the distance travelled with an empty barrow, the ratio or proportion of stones, sand and cement used.

A Lesson for Every Day
Maths
10–11 Years
© A&C Black

Nutrition numbers

On food packets the nutritional value of the contents is shown.
The labels below give information for each item.

Amount per cracker		Amount per oatcake		Amount per cookie	
Energy	34 Kcal	Energy	79 Kcal	Energy	112 Kcal
Protein	0·9 g	Protein	1·8 g	Protein	5·7 g
Carbohydrate	5·4 g	Carbohydrate	9·7 g	Carbohydrate	8·8 g
Fat	1·1 g	Fat	4·5 g	Fat	3·5 g
Fibre	0·3 g	Fibre	1·4 g	Fibre	0·9 g
Sodium	0·1 g	Sodium	0·08 g	Sodium	0·07 g

- **Use mental methods to answer these questions.**

1. How many grams of **sodium** would you have if you ate:

    4 crackers? _0·4g_   5 oatcakes? _____   3 cookies? _____

2. How many grams of **fibre** would you have if you ate:

    6 crackers? _____   8 oatcakes? _____   2 cookies? _____

3. How many grams of **fat** would you have if you ate:

    3 crackers? _____   7 oatcakes? _____   5 cookies? _____

4. How many grams of **carbohydrate** would you have if you ate:

    2 crackers? _____   9 oatcakes? _____   6 cookies? _____

5. How many grams of **protein** would you have if you ate:

    4 crackers? _____   8 oatcakes? _____   7 cookies? _____

6. How many kilocalories of **energy** would you have if you ate:

    5 crackers? _____   3 oatcakes? _____   9 cookies? _____

NOW TRY THIS!

- **How many oatcakes did you eat if you had 8·4 grams of fibre?** _____

Teachers' note Demonstrate appropriate strategies for multiplying decimals by single-digit numbers mentally, such as multiplying together two whole numbers and adjusting, or partitioning the decimal appropriately etc. The decimals could be altered to provide differentiation.

A Lesson for Every Day
Maths
10-11 Years
© A&C Black

Revolution solutions

These patterns are made from a range of shapes.
- Use what you know about angles around a point to find the value of the marked angle.

1.

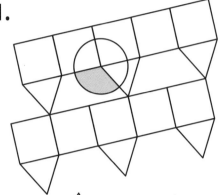

2.

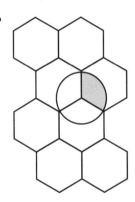

3.

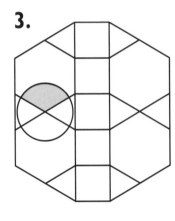

4.

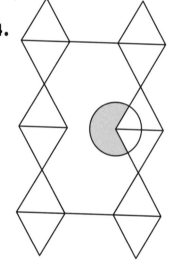

5.

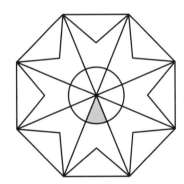

6.

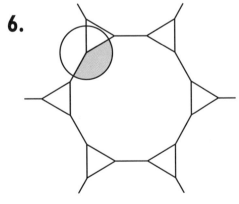

7.

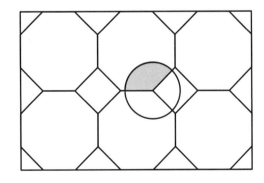

NOW TRY THIS!
- Talk to a partner about how you worked out each answer.

Teachers' note Demonstrate simpler examples to get the children started (see page 9). Encourage them to use their knowledge that angles around a point are 360° and to see if other angles are right angles (such as those in squares) or 60° (those in equilateral triangles). Also encourage them to see equal angles and to divide angles into equal parts. Provide calculators if needed.

A Lesson for Every Day
Maths
10–11 Years
© A&C Black

Micro dominoes

- **Work with a partner.**

☆ Cut out the domino pieces.

☆ Join them together so that touching
  measurements match. Start with the grey piece.

☆ Glue them onto paper in order.

3·24 m	136 cm	4 m	1640 m	200 mm	47 cm	1·22 m	500 m
90 mm	5 cm	0·5 km	1500 m	0·12 km	400 cm	0·47 m	324 cm
281 cm	122 cm	1·36 m	244 mm	0·7 m	19 mm	0·24 m	24 mm
0·12 m	45 cm	5·6 cm	2·81 m	8 cm	800 mm	0·7 cm	1·1 m
2·4 cm	888 cm	7 km	32 cm	0·1 m	100 m	0·3 m	12 cm
1·4 cm	7 m	1·64 km	1 mm	0·5 m	900 mm	24·4 cm	1·05 m
0·32 m	400 m	0·05 m	30 cm	700 cm	70 cm	240 cm	56 mm
105 cm	24 cm	1·5 km	7000 m	8·88 m	9 cm	80 cm	500 mm
110 cm	13 mm	450 mm	7 mm	0·1 cm	10 cm	0·1 km	80 mm
1·9 cm	2·4 m	0·4 km	120 m	1·3 cm	14 mm	0·9 m	0·2 m

Teachers' note Remind the children of the relationships between the standard metric units of length,
for example 1000 m = 1 km, 100 cm = 1 m, 10 mm = 1 cm. This activity can be quite challenging for
children so they should work in pairs or small groups to complete the task.

A Lesson for Every Day
Maths
10–11 Years
© A&C Black

Angle tangle

- Use a ruler to join the numbers in order.
- Estimate the size of each angle created.
- Use a protractor to check your answers.

a 2

8
k

j   i

h

7

g

10

4

1   m

c

f

b

l

d

5

e

3

q

6

	a	b	c	d	e	f	g	h	i	j	k	l	m
• **Estimate**													
• **Measure**													

NOW TRY THIS!

- Make your own dot-to-dot puzzles.
- Estimate and measure the angles.

Teachers' note Encourage the children to draw the lines accurately using a sharpened pencil to join the dots. Then encourage accurate measuring. The answers given on page 215 can be read to the children at the end so that they can see how accurately they are measuring angles using a protractor or angle measurer.

A Lesson for Every Day
Maths
10-11 Years
© A&C Black

They do, duvet?

- **Without using a protractor, write the missing angles.**

  Remember that the angles inside a triangle add up to **180°**.

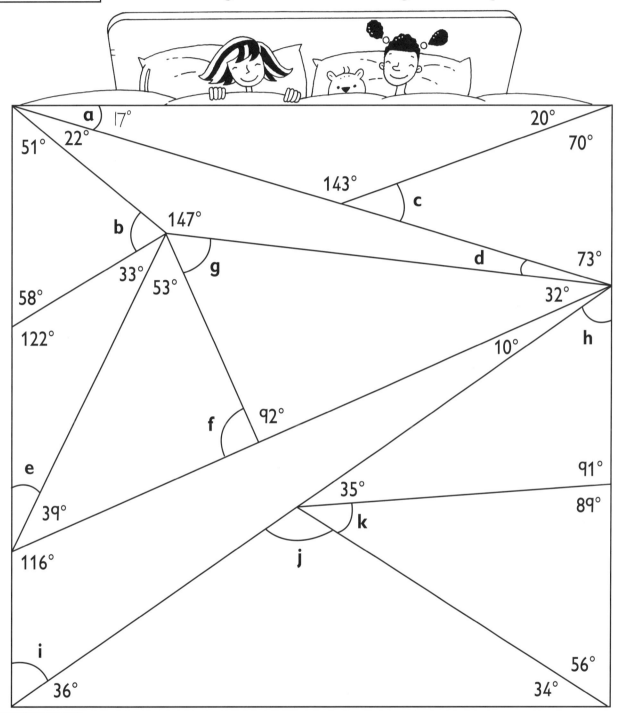

Teachers' note Demonstrate how the angles of a triangle can be torn off and rearranged to make a straight line, thus showing that the angles have a sum of 180°. To make this activity more complex some angles can be masked before copying. See page 17 for further details.

A Lesson for Every Day
Maths
10–11 Years
© A&C Black

147

Get to the point

- ## Without using a protractor, write the missing angles.
  Remember that the angles around a point have a sum of 360°.

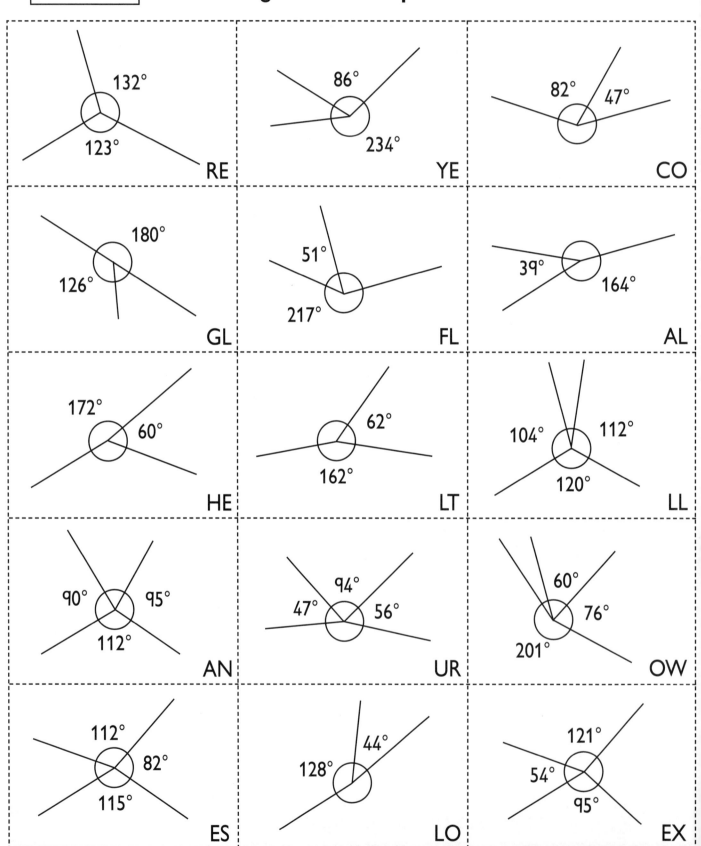

132° 123° **RE**	86° 234° **YE**	82° 47° **CO**
180° 126° **GL**	51° 217° **FL**	39° 164° **AL**
172° 60° **HE**	62° 162° **LT**	104° 112° 120° **LL**
90° 95° 112° **AN**	94° 47° 56° **UR**	60° 76° 201° **OW**
112° 82° 115° **ES**	128° 44° **LO**	121° 54° 95° **EX**

Teachers' note As an extension activity, the children should cut out the cards and put them in order, from largest to smallest, according to the missing angle they have written. They should then work out what the letters of the sentence spell and follow the instruction.

A Lesson for Every Day
Maths
10–11 Years
© A&C Black

Coded coordinates

• **Plot these coordinates on the grid and label them.**

A (11, 17)

B (5, 14)

C (11, 14)

D (12, 12)

E (8, 11)

F (14, 11)

G (18, 6)

H (8, 8)

I (2, 2)

J (14, 2)

K (18, 19)

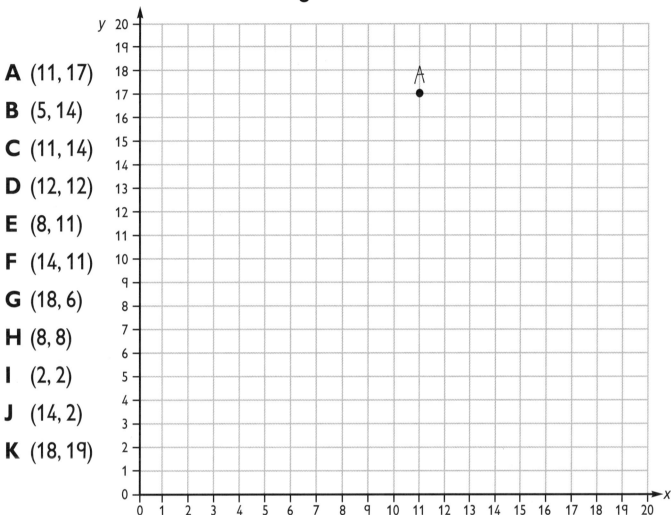

• **Write the letters of the coordinates you have plotted that form the vertices of:**

(a) a square _____

(b) a rectangle _____

(c) a parallelogram _____

(d) a right-angled scalene triangle _____

(e) a trapezium _____

NOW TRY THIS!

A parallelogram has vertices marked at I, J and G.
• **What are the coordinates of its fourth vertex?** _____

Teachers' note Point out that there may be more than one solution to each question. Encourage the children to use all the letters of the points in their answers. Further extension questions could be asked to encourage the children to identify the fourth vertex of a described quadrilateral, given three of its vertices.

A Lesson for Every Day
Maths
10-11 Years
© A&C Black

Coordinate puzzles

- **Cut out the puzzle strips at the bottom of this sheet.**
- **Use a grid to solve each puzzle.**

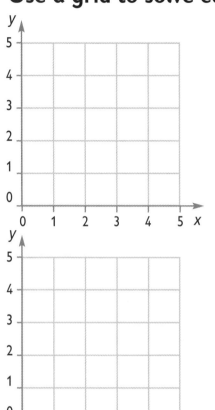

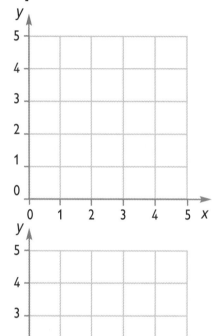

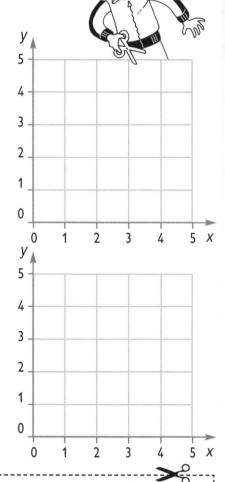

Draw an isosceles triangle with one vertex at (2, 0) and another at (5, 3).
Write the coordinates of its third vertex. (__, __)

Draw a square with no horizontal or vertical lines.
Write its area. _____

Draw a rectangle with an area of 12 cm² that has a vertex at (3, 5).
Write the coordinates of its other vertices. (__, __) (__, __) (__, __)

Draw a parallelogram with no horizontal or vertical lines and no right angles.
Write the coordinates of its vertices. (__, __) (__, __) (__, __) (__, __)

Draw three different-sized symmetrical trapeziums. Write the coordinates of
the vertices of the largest one. (__, __) (__, __) (__, __) (__, __)

Draw a rectangle with one vertex at (2, 0) and another at (4, 1).
Write the coordinates of the other two vertices. (__, __) (__, __)

A Lesson for Every Day
Maths
10–11 Years
© A&C Black

Reflection selection

- **Reflect each shape in the dotted mirror line.**
- **Write the coordinates of the vertices of the shape and its reflection.**

1.

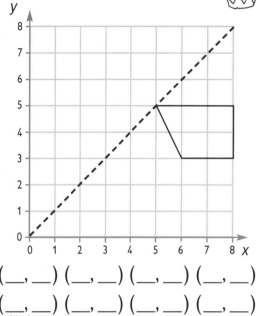

original shape (__ , __) (__ , __) (__ , __) (__ , __)
reflection (__ , __) (__ , __) (__ , __) (__ , __)

2.

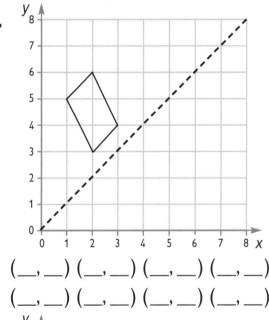

(__ , __) (__ , __) (__ , __) (__ , __)
(__ , __) (__ , __) (__ , __) (__ , __)

3.

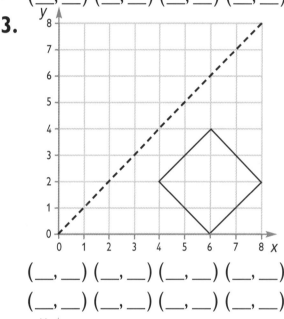

(__ , __) (__ , __) (__ , __) (__ , __)
(__ , __) (__ , __) (__ , __) (__ , __)

4.

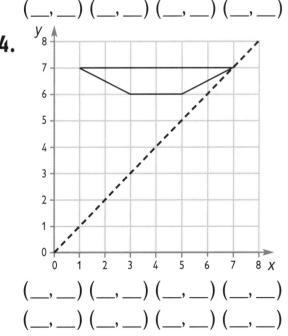

(__ , __) (__ , __) (__ , __) (__ , __)
(__ , __) (__ , __) (__ , __) (__ , __)

5.

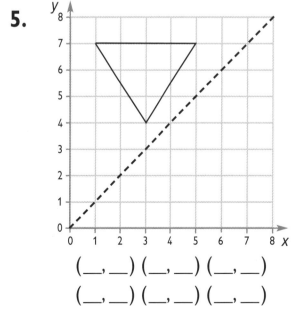

(__ , __) (__ , __) (__ , __)
(__ , __) (__ , __) (__ , __)

Teachers' note Discuss strategies for reflection (see page 18). Encourage the children to say what they notice about the coordinates and then to use this to help them check their answers. Stress that this pattern only works for the mirror line $y = x$.

A Lesson for Every Day
Maths
10-11 Years
© A&C Black

Rotation station: 1

- **Plot and join the points in order to make a shape.**
- **Then rotate each shape as described.**

1.

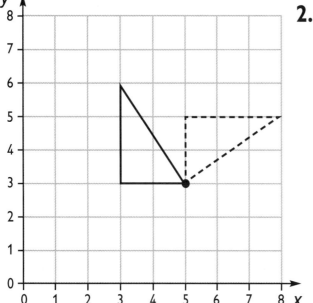

(a) $(3, 3)$ $(3, 6)$ $(5, 3)$ $(3, 3)$

(b) Rotate it about the point $(5, 3)$ through 90° clockwise.

2.

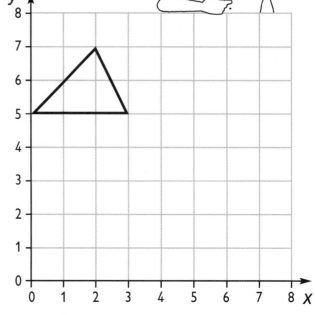

(a) $(0, 5)$ $(2, 7)$ $(3, 5)$ $(0, 5)$

(b) Rotate it about the point $(3, 5)$ through 180° clockwise.

3.

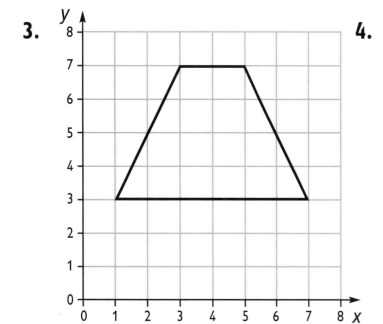

(a) $(1, 3)$ $(3, 7)$ $(5, 7)$ $(7, 3)$ $(1, 3)$

(b) Rotate it about the point $(4, 5)$ through 180° clockwise.

4.

(a) $(2, 4)$ $(4, 6)$ $(5, 5)$ $(5, 3)$ $(3, 3)$ $(2, 4)$

(b) Rotate it about the point $(5, 3)$ through 90° anticlockwise.

Teachers' note Provide the children with a sheet of tracing paper. Demonstrate how to trace the shape, place the pencil onto the centre of rotation and then gently turn the tracing paper before tracing the shape into its new position. As an extension, the children could make up their own questions for a partner to solve, ensuring that the rotation is possible within the grid.

152

A Lesson for Every Day
Maths
10-11 Years
© A&C Black

Rotation station: 2

- **Plot and join the points in order to make a shape.**
- **Then rotate each shape as described.**

1.

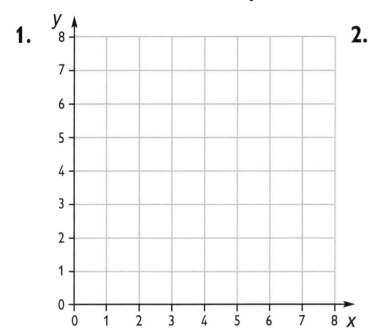

(a) (1, 7) (3, 6) (4, 4) (2, 5) (1, 7)

(b) Rotate it about the point (4, 4) through 90° clockwise.

2.

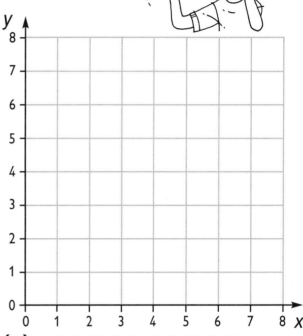

(a) (2, 4) (3, 6) (4, 6) (4, 3) (2, 4)

(b) Rotate it about the point (2, 4) through 180° anticlockwise.

3.

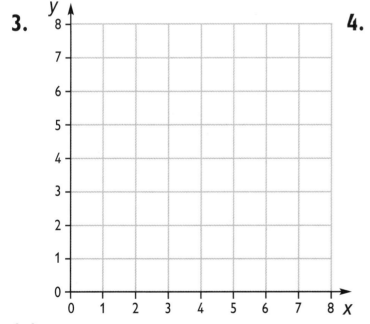

(a) (3, 2) (2, 5) (3, 5) (4, 6) (5, 5) (6, 5) (5, 2) (3, 2)

(b) Rotate it about the point (4, 4) through 180° clockwise.

4.

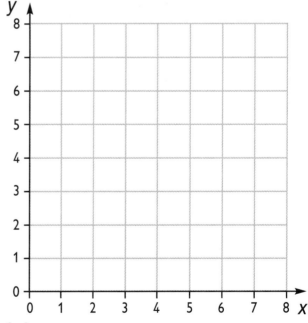

(a) (2, 4) (5, 4) (5, 1) (4, 3) (2, 4)

(b) Rotate it about the point (2, 4) through 90° anticlockwise.

Teachers' note Provide the children with a sheet of tracing paper. Demonstrate how to trace the shape, place the pencil onto the centre of rotation and then gently turn the tracing paper before tracing the shape into its new position. As an extension, the children could make up their own questions for a partner to solve, ensuring that the rotation is possible within the grid.

A Lesson for Every Day
Maths
10–11 Years
© A&C Black

Dimitri's day

Dimitri travels from house to house, fitting
and repairing electrical equipment.
Here is his schedule for the day.

Job	Time
1 Deliver and fit satellite dish	9:00
2 Repair washing machine	10:15
3 Adjust TV aerial	11:50
4 Deliver and set up computer	12:20
5 Mend broken oven light	14:15
6 Fix music system	15:05

1 Write how much time Dimitri has planned for:

   a job 2 <u>1 hr 35 mins</u>   **b** job 4 _____   **c** job 5 _____

2 He finishes job 1 by 9:37 and it takes him 20 minutes to
reach job 2. How many minutes early does he arrive? _____

3 He finishes job 2 by 11:28. How long does
he have to reach job 3? _____

4 Because of a traffic jam, he does not arrive at job 3
until 12:04. How many minutes late is he? _____

5 At half past 12 he collects the computer for job 4 and
reaches the house 18 minutes later to deliver it.
How many minutes late is he? _____

6 He arrives on time for job 5 and he mends
the light in 28 minutes. How many minutes
does he have to reach job 6? _____

7 He arrives on time for job 6 and finishes 1 hour and 25 minutes
later. At what time does he finish? _____

NOW TRY THIS!

**Dimitri is paid £3.50 for every 15 minutes he works.
He is paid from 9:00 am until the time he finishes.**
• **How much will he be paid?** _____

154

Teachers' note Encourage the children to describe how they worked out each answer and to describe
any difficulties they encountered. For the extension, ask them to write the calculations they used to
work out the answer.

A Lesson for Every Day
Maths
10-11 Years
© A&C Black

Scale drawings

- Measure the length and width of each picture in centimetres.
- Now divide each measurement by the number shown and use a ruler to draw a new picture reduced in size onto a blank piece of paper.

1.

5·6 cm

6·4 cm

Divide by 4

2.

Divide by 7

3.

Divide by 3

4.

Divide by 6

5.

Divide by 6

Teachers' note Children will be getting practice in dividing U.t by U for this activity and will develop an understanding of scale factors for enlarging or reducing the size of shapes. Encourage the children to carefully draw the new rectangles onto paper.

A Lesson for Every Day
Maths
10-11 Years
© A&C Black

Gemstone necklace

Each gem represents a different decimal with two digits.
- **Work out which decimal each gem stands
  for and fill in any missing answers.**

1.  **+** (2·7) **= 10·2**   **– ◯ = 4·8**

 **× 3 = _____**   **÷ 5 = _____**

2. **+ ◠ = 13·8**   **– ◠ = 3·2**

 × 4 = _____   **÷ 5 = _____**

3. **+ ◯ = 15·7**   **– ◯ = 3·1**

 × 5 = _____   **÷ 2 = _____**

4. **+ ▽ = 16·8**   **– ▽ = 1·6**

 **× 6 = _____**   **÷ 4 = _____**

NOW TRY THIS!
- **Make up some gem puzzles of your own for a
  partner to solve.**

Teachers' note This activity involves adding, subtracting, multiplying and dividing decimals mentally. Encourage the children to discuss their strategies for finding the value of each gem and to explain the mental methods they used to calculate the other values.

A Lesson for Every Day
Maths
10–11 Years
© A&C Black

Erin's errors

Erin has made a mistake in every calculation!

• Find the error and correct the calculation.
Use estimation to help you.

Where did I go wrong? Talk to a partner.

---

1. 923 ÷ 8

```
8 ) 923        100
  − 800    8 × 10
    123
  −  80    8 × 10
     43
  −  40    8 × 5
      3
```
                    115 r3
Answer: ~~25 r3~~

---

2. 467 ÷ 9

```
9 ) 467
  − 450    9 × 50
     17
  −   9    9 × 1
      8
```

Answer: **51**

---

3. 294 ÷ 6

```
6 ) 294
  − 240    6 × 400
     54
  −  54    6 × 9
```

Answer: **409**

---

4. 852 ÷ 7

```
7 ) 852
  − 700    7 × 100
    152
  − 120    7 × 20
     32
  −  28    7 × 4
      4
```

Answer: **124 r4**

---

5. 762 ÷ 8

```
8 ) 762
  − 720    8 × 90
     42
  −  42    8 × 6
      0
```

Answer: **96**

---

6. 845 ÷ 9

```
9 ) 845
  − 810    9 × 90
     25
  −  18    9 × 2
      7
```

Answer: **99 r7**

---

7. 846 ÷ 23

```
23 ) 846
   − 690    23 × 30
     156
   − 115    23 × 5
      41
   −  23    23 × 1
      18
```

Answer: **18 r36**

---

8. 787 ÷ 35

```
35 ) 787
   − 700    35 × 20
      87
   −  80    35 × 2
       7
```

Answer: **22 r7**

---

9. 994 ÷ 41

```
41 ) 994
   − 820    41 × 20
     174
   − 164    41 × 4
      10
```

Answer: **24**

Teachers' note This method of division, known as 'chunking', is useful in helping children to divide when the divisor has two digits, for example questions 7–9 on this sheet. As an extension, ask the children to use a calculator and inverses to check their final answers.

A Lesson for Every Day
Maths
10–11 Years
© A&C Black

Time after time

- **Use a calculator to solve each problem.**

Work with a partner.

1.

A swimming session is 1 hour and 10 minutes. To earn a certificate, children have to attend sessions for 840 minutes. How many sessions is this?

2.

A gymnastics class lasts for 50 minutes. Jo attends 7 classes. How many hours and minutes is this?

3.

A quick sponge takes $2\frac{1}{4}$ minutes to mix, 25 minutes to bake and 45 seconds to eat! How long from start to finish?

4.

A microwave oven cooks for $2\frac{1}{2}$ minutes on medium power, 75 seconds on low power and $3\frac{1}{4}$ minutes on high power. How long is it on for?

5.

A dance teacher teaches a class for 1 hour and 17 minutes. She has a half-hour break, then teaches for another 45 minutes. How long does all this take?

6.

A computer session is 1 hour and 30 minutes. To earn a certificate, students have to attend sessions for 810 minutes. How many sessions is this?

7.

Callum plays football for 35 minutes a day, 5 days a week. How many hours and how many minutes does he play in 7 weeks?

8.

A karate instructor teaches a class for $1\frac{1}{2}$ hours. He has a 40-minute break, then teaches for another $1\frac{1}{4}$ hours. How long does all this take?

9.

COMING SOON: *KING COD*

At a cinema, the trailers play for 35 seconds, 8 minutes and $1\frac{1}{4}$ minutes. For how long in total do they play?

158

Teachers' note When the children are using a calculator and dealing with time calculations, it is important to remind them to convert the times to the same unit, for example minutes, and to interpret the display correctly, multiplying any decimal digits by 60 where necessary.

A Lesson for Every Day
Maths
10–11 Years
© A&C Black

Quick conversions

- **To find each missing number, do <u>one</u> of these things:**

A	Multiply by 10.
B	Multiply by 100.
C	Multiply by 1000.
D	Divide by 10.
E	Divide by 100.
F	Divide by 1000.

- **Cut out the cards and work with a partner to sort them into groups A, B, C, D, E or F. Fill in the missing numbers.**

5·2 cm = _____ mm	7·09 km = _____ m
16 cm = _____ m	2040 m = _____ km
87 mm = _____ cm	7·34 kg = _____ g
350 g = _____ kg	4·12 m = _____ cm
0·01 l = _____ ml	3·8 cm = _____ mm
6·72 km = _____ m	0·09 kg = _____ g
620 l = _____ ml	50 m = _____ km
32 m = _____ cm	5482 mm = _____ cm
7600 g = _____ kg	108 cm = _____ m
0·08 m = _____ cm	4·05 l = _____ ml
7 mm = _____ cm	49·7 m = _____ mm

Teachers' note Children should work in pairs for this activity to encourage discussion. As an extension activity, ask the children to make up their own puzzle cards like these.

A Lesson for Every Day
Maths
10-11 Years
© A&C Black

Full scale ahead

• **Read each scale, giving your answer to the degree of accuracy shown.**

1. to the nearest 100 ml

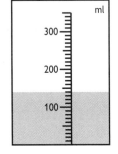

2. to the nearest 10 kg

3. to the nearest 10 ml

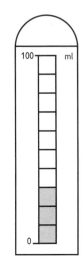

5. to the nearest 500 g

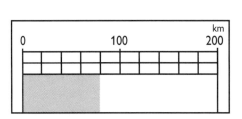

4. to the nearest 100 g

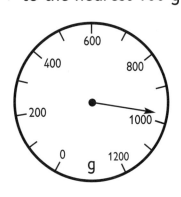

6. to the nearest 100 km

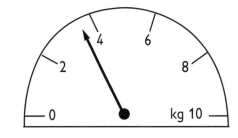

7. to the nearest 5 kg

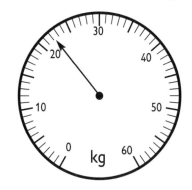

8. to the nearest 0·1 m

| | 10 | 20 | 30 | 40 | 50 | 60 | 70 | 80 | 90 | cm |

NOW TRY THIS!

• **A bag of fruit was labelled 5 kg when measured to the nearest kg. What is the smallest amount that the bag could have weighed?** _____

Teachers' note This activity encourages the children to appreciate that measurement is approximate and that it is important to know the degree of accuracy to which you are recording a reading.

A Lesson for Every Day
Maths
10-11 Years
© A&C Black

Rubber sizes

A class have collected together all the rubbers they could find.

- Work out the length of each rubber.

1.

RUBBER
12000
...

Rubber

0 1 2 3 4 5 6 7

2.

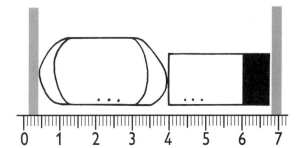

0 1 2 3 4 5 6 7

3.

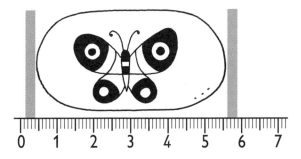

0 1 2 3 4 5 6 7

4.

DESIGN

0 1 2 3 4 5 6 7

5.

FOR **BIG** MISTAKES

0 1 2 3 4 5 6 7

6.

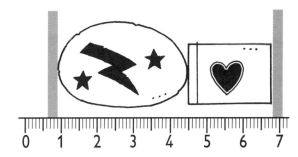

0 1 2 3 4 5 6 7

7.

FOR TINY MISTAKES

0 1 2 3 4 5 6 7

8.

R ubber

0 1 2 3 4 5 6 7

NOW TRY THIS!

- Measure the length and width of some of the rubbers in your own classroom.

Teachers' note Encourage the children to measure the lengths to the nearest millimetre (or tenth of a centimetre) and then to use subtraction to find the length of each rubber.

A Lesson for Every Day
Maths
10–11 Years
© A&C Black

Half squares

Each of these shows half a square shaded:

      Each shows $\frac{1}{2}$ cm².

Two of the half squares make one whole square.

• Use this to help you find the area of each pattern.

a _____   b _____   c _____   d _____

e _____   f _____   g _____   h _____

i _____   j _____   k _____   l _____

Teachers' note This activity encourages the children to begin to join part squares together to form wholes. This is an important step in being able to accurately predict the areas of irregular shapes.

A Lesson for Every Day
Maths
10–11 Years
© A&C Black

Something fishy

- **Estimate the area of each fish in squares.**
- **Count to check.**

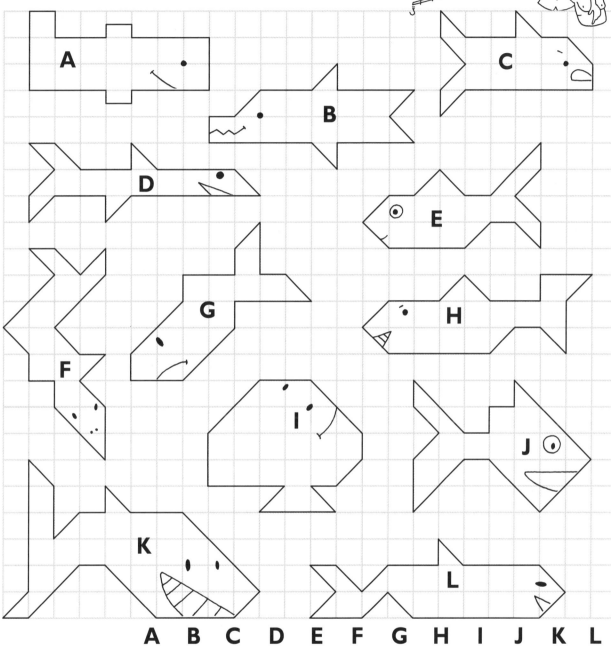

	A	B	C	D	E	F	G	H	I	J	K	L
Estimate												
Check												

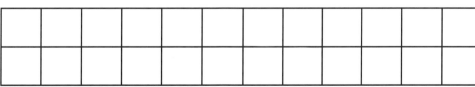

NOW TRY THIS!

- **Draw three more fish of your own on squared paper.**
- **Estimate their areas then count to check.**

Teachers' note The children should be encouraged to mark the squares and half squares as they count them. Watch out for those children who count half squares as whole squares.

A Lesson for Every Day
Maths
10-11 Years
© A&C Black

Carpet calculations

This is the plan of **Mrs Jones's house.**

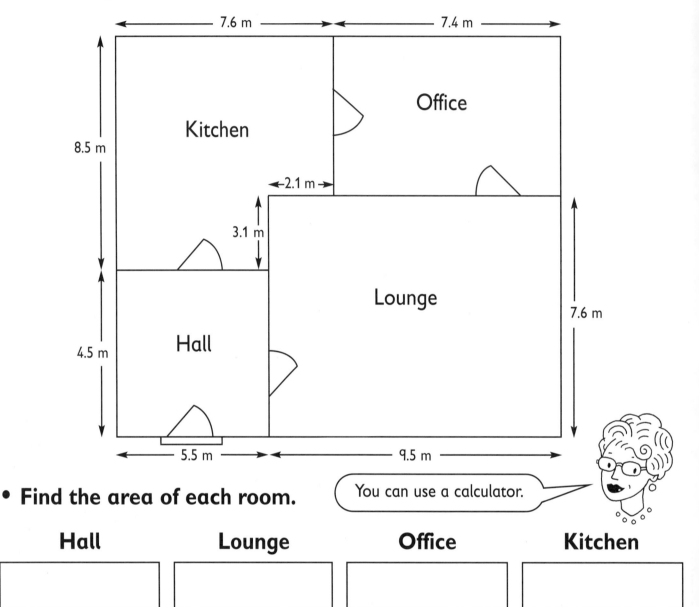

- **Find the area of each room.**

You can use a calculator.

Hall	**Lounge**	**Office**	**Kitchen**

NOW TRY THIS!

Mrs Jones decides to have different carpets in each room. Here are the prices of the different carpets.

- **Work out how much money Mrs Jones will pay in total.**

(a) Hall £12.20 per m^2 _____

(b) Lounge £9.95 per m^2 _____

(c) Office £8.45 per m^2 _____

(d) Kitchen £11.49 per m^2 _____   **Total** _____

Teachers' note Ensure that the children have a calculator and a ruler each for this activity. Remind the children of the formula for finding the area of a rectangle and encourage them to split the kitchen up into two rectangles.

A Lesson for Every Day
Maths
10-11 Years
© A&C Black

Fun at the fair

At the school fair, you are told the **total amount of money under two cups. You win the money if you guess which coins are under the cups.**

Rule 1 There can only be one type of coin under each cup.
Rule 2 The same number of coins must be under both cups.

Example:

The total is **48p.**

$4 \times$ 10p $4 \times$ 2p

• **Work out which coins are under the cups.**

1 The total is **£1.25**. _____ _____	**2** The total is **£1.80**. _____ _____
3 The total is **£11.22**. _____ _____	**4** The total is **£9.09**. _____ _____
5 The total is **£3.64**. _____ _____	**6** The total is **£2.25**. _____ _____

NOW TRY THIS!

• **Write an explanation to tell someone else how you solved each problem.**

Teachers' note The focus of this activity should be on the children describing and explaining how they tackled this type of question. Encourage them to show others their working, and to talk about what they might do differently if they were doing this again. As a further extension, the children could make up their own 'cup' problems for a partner to solve.

A Lesson for Every Day
Maths
10–11 Years
© A&C Black

Dancing dilemma

- **How can you organise the information in this problem?**

Mrs Pandit says: I will only dance if Mr Taki dances.

Mr Harris says: I will dance, whoever dances.

Mrs Mills says: I won't dance if Miss Jones dances.

Miss Lee says: I won't dance if Mrs Mills dances.

Mr Taki says: I will only dance if Miss Jones dances.

Mr Fox says: I will dance if Mrs Pandit dances.

Miss Jones says: I won't dance if Mr Harris dances.

Mr Simpson says: I will dance, whoever dances.

- **Six people are on the dance floor. Who are they?**

- ✂

NOW TRY THIS!

The six people that are dancing begin to dance in pairs.
- **Use the statements below to find out who dances with whom. Record your answers on the back of this sheet.**

 Each female dances with a male.

Miss Jones will **not** pair up with Mr Taki.

 Mrs Pandit pairs up with Mr Simpson.

Teachers' note Cut off the extension activity before giving the worksheet to the children. Ask the children to demonstrate how they represented or worked out this problem, and compare different approaches used by different children. Encourage them to check their solution against each clue to be sure that all are satisfied.

A Lesson for Every Day
Maths
10–11 Years
© A&C Black

Talking points: 1

- **Cut out the cards and discuss each situation with a partner.**

1 If you multiply a number by 5, can the answer be an **even number**?

If it is possible, what does this mean the original number must be?

2 If you divide a number by 5, can the answer be a **whole number**?

If it is possible, what does this mean the original number must be?

3 If you add 1 to a number, can the answer be an **odd number**?

If it is possible, what does this mean the original number must be?

4 If you multiply a number by 3, can the answer be an **even number**?

If it is possible, what does this mean the original number must be?

5 If you subtract 1 from a number, can the answer be a **multiple of 5**?

If it is possible, what does this mean the original number must be?

6 If you divide a number by 2, can the answer be an **even number**?

If it is possible, what does this mean the original number must be?

7 If you divide a number by 3, can the answer be an **even number**?

If it is possible, what does this mean the original number must be?

8 If you multiply a number by 4, can the answer be an **odd number**?

If it is possible, what does this mean the original number must be?

9 If you multiply a number by 3, can the answer be a **multiple of 6**?

If it is possible, what does this mean the original number must be?

10 If you divide a number by 4, can the answer be an **even number**?

If it is possible, what does this mean the original number must be?

Teachers' note Use in conjunction with 'Talking points: 2', which can be used as an extension activity or for differentiation. Ask the children to give examples on the back of each card to justify their reasoning.

A Lesson for Every Day
Maths
10–11 Years
© A&C Black

Talking points: 2

- **Cut out the cards and discuss each situation with a partner.**

1 If you add 3 to a number and then multiply by 5, can the answer be an **even number**? If it is possible, what does this mean the original number must be?	**2** If you add 3 to a number and then divide by 5, can the answer be a **whole number**? If it is possible, what does this mean the original number must be?
3 If you add 1 to a number and then multiply by 2, can the answer be an **odd number**? If it is possible, what does this mean the original number must be?	**4** If you add 1 to a number and then divide by 2, can the answer be a **whole number**? If it is possible, what does this mean the original number must be?
5 If you subtract 1 from a number and then divide by 10, can the answer be a **whole number**? If it is possible, what does this mean the original number must be?	**6** If you subtract 2 from a number and then divide by 5, can the answer be a **whole number**? If it is possible, what does this mean the original number must be?
7 If you add 2 to a number and then multiply by 3, can the answer be an **even number**? If it is possible, what does this mean the original number must be?	**8** If you add 1 to a number and then multiply by 3, can the answer be an **odd number**? If it is possible, what does this mean the original number must be?
9 If you double a number and then add 1, can the answer be an **even number**? If it is possible, what does this mean the original number must be?	**10** If you multiply a number by 3 and then divide by 2, can the answer be an **even number**? If it is possible, what does this mean the original number must be?

Teachers' note Use in conjunction with 'Talking points: 1'. Ask the children to give examples on the back of each card to justify their reasoning.

A Lesson for Every Day
Maths
10-11 Years
© A&C Black

- **Find how many of each animal there are in the field.**
- **Discuss with a partner how to solve each problem.**

In field A: $\frac{3}{8}$ of the animals are horses

$\frac{1}{4}$ of the animals are cows

$\frac{1}{16}$ of the animals are sheep.

There are $\boxed{5}$ goats.

In field B: $\frac{1}{10}$ of the animals are horses

$\frac{1}{3}$ of the animals are cows

$\frac{5}{12}$ of the animals are sheep.

There are $\boxed{9}$ goats.

In field C: $\frac{2}{7}$ of the animals are horses

$\frac{1}{5}$ of the animals are cows

$\frac{1}{3}$ of the animals are sheep.

There are $\boxed{19}$ goats.

NOW TRY THIS!

- **Write an explanation to tell someone else how you solved each problem.**

Teachers' note Encourage the children to change the fractions to those with common denominators to help them solve these puzzles. As a further extension, invite the children to write new puzzles of this type and to explain how each could be solved.

A Lesson for Every Day
Maths
10-11 Years
© A&C Black

Copy cats

Emma is photocopying a picture to change its size. The measurements of the original picture are shown.

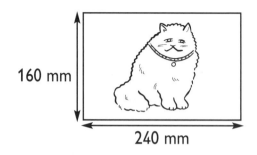

160 mm

240 mm

- Follow the descriptions below to find the size of the final picture.

1. First, Emma sets the photocopier to 50%.
   The lengths of the new picture are 50% of the original.

2. Then she sets the photocopier to 150%.
   She photocopies the **new picture** (not the original).

3. Then she sets the photocopier to 50%.
   She photocopies the **most recent picture produced**.

4. Finally, she sets the photocopier to 110%.
   She photocopies the **most recent picture produced**.

Show your workings here.

NOW TRY THIS!

- **Repeat the investigation for this picture:**

200 mm

300 mm

Teachers' note Ensure the children appreciate that a photocopier can be used to enlarge and reduce lengths, and that they understand how to work out 50%, 150%, etc of a number. As a further extension, they could work out the areas of the pictures and investigate how the areas do not increase/decrease by the percentage shown, but rather by the percentage squared.

A Lesson for Every Day
Maths
10–11 Years
© A&C Black

Planet exploration

If you were to visit different planets, your weight would change.

- **Follow the instructions to find how much each person would weigh on different planets.**

Use a written method.

To find a person's weight on **Mercury**, multiply their Earth weight by **0·3**.

To find a person's weight on **Venus**, multiply their Earth weight by **0·9**.

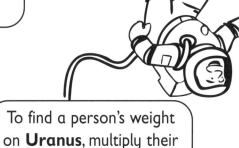

To find a person's weight on **Uranus**, multiply their Earth weight by **0·8**.

To find a person's weight on **Mars**, multiply their Earth weight by **0·4**.

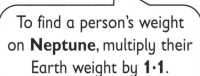

To find a person's weight on **Neptune**, multiply their Earth weight by **1·1**.

To find a person's weight on **Jupiter**, multiply their Earth weight by **2·4**.

	Earth	Mercury	Venus	Uranus	Mars	Neptune	Jupiter
James	37 kg						
Chloe	46 kg						
Ali	62 kg						

NOW TRY THIS!

- **Weigh yourself and then calculate what you would weigh on each planet. Write it in the table above.**

Teachers' note Ensure that the children make an estimate before calculating and use it to check whether their answer is a sensible one. When estimating the size of an answer, encourage the children to round the numbers appropriately. Provide the children with paper on which to show their written methods.

A Lesson for Every Day
Maths
10–11 Years
© A&C Black

Pack it in

- **Using the information in the box, give your answer as an improper fraction and as a mixed number.**

6 pots of yoghurt in one pack.

4 tins of beans in one pack.

5 bagels in one bag.

10 chunks of chocolate in one bar.

8 equal slices in one pizza.

- **What fraction of:**

1 a pack of yogurt is 7 pots?

$\dfrac{7}{6}$ $\quad$ $1\dfrac{1}{6}$

2 a chocolate bar is 13 chunks?

3 a pack of beans is 9 tins?

4 a pizza is 13 slices?

5 a bag of bagels is 14 bagels?

6 a pack of yogurt is 17 pots?

7 a chocolate bar is 27 chunks?

8 a pack of beans is 13 tins?

NOW TRY THIS!

- **Write these fractions as mixed numbers in their simplest form.**

$\dfrac{38}{6}$ $\qquad$ $\dfrac{38}{4}$ $\qquad$ $\dfrac{38}{5}$ $\qquad$ $\dfrac{38}{10}$

Teachers' note It is important that children realise that each of the different wholes in the box have been split into a different number of equal parts. Thus when they decide what fraction of the whole is being described they must refer to the box to decide what the denominator of the improper fraction and mixed number will be.

172

A Lesson for Every Day
Maths
10-11 Years
© A&C Black

How are we related?

These two children are describing their shirt number in relation to the other's shirt number.

My number is $\frac{9}{10}$ of your number.

My number is $1\frac{1}{9}$ times your number.

- **Fill in the missing fractions or mixed numbers in these statements.**

1

My number is _____ of your number.

My number is _____ times your number.

2

My number is _____ of your number.

My number is _____ times your number.

3

My number is _____ of your number.

My number is _____ times your number.

4

My number is _____ of your number.

My number is _____ times your number.

5

My number is _____ of your number.

My number is _____ times your number.

NOW TRY THIS!

- **With a partner, choose a number each and write two statements about them in relation to each other.**

Teachers' note When finding the mixed number, children might find it easier to first write an improper fraction and then to convert it to a mixed number i.e. for the example at the top of the page the improper fraction $\frac{10}{9}$ is then converted to $1\frac{1}{9}$.

A Lesson for Every Day
Maths
10-11 Years
© A&C Black

Fraction quiz

In this quiz, a point is scored for each correct answer.

- Tick the correct answers. There may be more than one each time.
- Work out Millie's, Billy's and Lily's scores at the end.

M   B   L

#	Question	M	B	L
1	How many weeks is 15 days?	$2\frac{2}{7}$	$1\frac{1}{15}$	$2\frac{1}{7}$
2	How many weeks is 30 days?	$3\frac{2}{7}$	$4\frac{1}{2}$	$4\frac{2}{7}$
3	How many dozen is 41 eggs?	$3\frac{5}{12}$	$3\frac{1}{2}$	$3\frac{7}{12}$
4	How many years is 18 months?	$1\frac{6}{12}$	$1\frac{1}{2}$	$2\frac{1}{4}$
5	How many dozen is 54 eggs?	$4\frac{6}{12}$	$4\frac{1}{12}$	$4\frac{1}{2}$
6	How many days is 60 hours?	$2\frac{3}{4}$	$2\frac{12}{24}$	$2\frac{1}{2}$
7	How many years is 26 months?	$3\frac{3}{12}$	$2\frac{1}{12}$	$2\frac{1}{6}$
8	How many weeks is 47 days?	$6\frac{5}{7}$	$6\frac{4}{7}$	$5\frac{5}{7}$
9	How many dozen is 50 eggs?	$4\frac{1}{6}$	$4\frac{1}{2}$	$4\frac{2}{12}$
10	How many days is 36 hours?	$3\frac{1}{12}$	$1\frac{12}{24}$	$1\frac{1}{2}$

Scores _____ _____ _____

NOW TRY THIS!

- **Complete these statements with mixed numbers.**

  29 days is _____ weeks   29 eggs is _____ dozen

174

Teachers' note At the start of the lesson revise how many of each smaller unit are in the larger unit, listing them on the board, i.e. 1 week = 7 days, 1 dozen = 12 eggs, 12 months = 1 year, 1 day = 24 hours. Emphasise that the answers should be mixed numbers and may also be in their simplest form.

A Lesson for Every Day
Maths
10–11 Years
© A&C Black

A sure measure

- **For each question, write the fraction as an** | improper fraction | **and as a** | mixed number |
in its simplest form.

1 What fraction of **1 metre** is each length?

a 150 cm $\frac{150}{100} = \frac{3}{2} = 1\frac{1}{2}$

b 225 cm _____

c 275 cm _____

d 310 cm _____

e 120 cm _____

f 290 cm _____

g 101 cm _____

h 135 cm _____

i 340 cm _____

j 260 cm _____

2 What fraction of **1 kilogram** is each weight?

a 1500 g $\frac{1500}{1000} = \frac{3}{2} = 1\frac{1}{2}$

b 2100 g _____

c 1001 g _____

d 1250 g _____

e 3750 g _____

f 2005 g _____

g 3200 g _____

h 1050 g _____

i 2350 g _____

j 4600 g _____

NOW TRY THIS!

- **What fraction of** | £1 | **is each of these?**

(a) £1.50 _____ **(b)** £2.25 _____ **(c)** £1.75 _____

(d) £3.10 _____ **(e)** £7.50 _____ **(f)** £4.20 _____

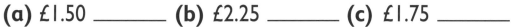

Teachers' note An alternative way to tackle this page is for the children to write the amount as a decimal (essentially converting the measurement to metres or kilograms). They could then convert the decimal to a mixed number, and then an improper fraction.

A Lesson for Every Day
Maths
10-11 Years
© A&C Black

Sorting session

- **Cut out the cards.**
- **Sort the cards into groups according to their answers.**

 $7\frac{1}{2}$ $6\frac{3}{4}$  $7\frac{5}{8}$  $6\frac{1}{2}$ $7\frac{5}{6}$ $6\frac{1}{3}$

$27 \div 4$	$\frac{1}{8}$ of 61	$\frac{54}{8}$
$13 \times \frac{1}{2}$	$\frac{60}{8}$	$\frac{1}{10}$ of 65
$30 \div 4$	$19 \times \frac{1}{3}$	$\frac{1}{8}$ of 52
$\frac{39}{6}$	$47 \div 6$	$15 \times \frac{1}{2}$
$26 \div 4$	$\frac{1}{6}$ of 38	$\frac{45}{6}$
$75 \times \frac{1}{10}$	$\frac{76}{12}$	$78 \div 12$

Teachers' note This activity encourages the children to appreciate the relationship between fractions and multiplication and division, for example that $6 \div 2 = \frac{1}{2}$ of $6 = 6 \times \frac{1}{2}$. The children should be reminded to simplify the fraction part of the mixed number where possible.

A Lesson for Every Day
Maths
10-11 Years
© A&C Black

Fraction satisfaction

• Play this game with a partner.

☆ Toss a coin to see who goes first.

☆ Take turns to choose a fraction and a whole number from the circle. Work out that fraction of the amount. This is your score. Now cover them both with a cube.

☆ Keep a running total. The winner is the player with the highest total when all the numbers are covered.

You need a coin, some cubes and paper to keep score on.

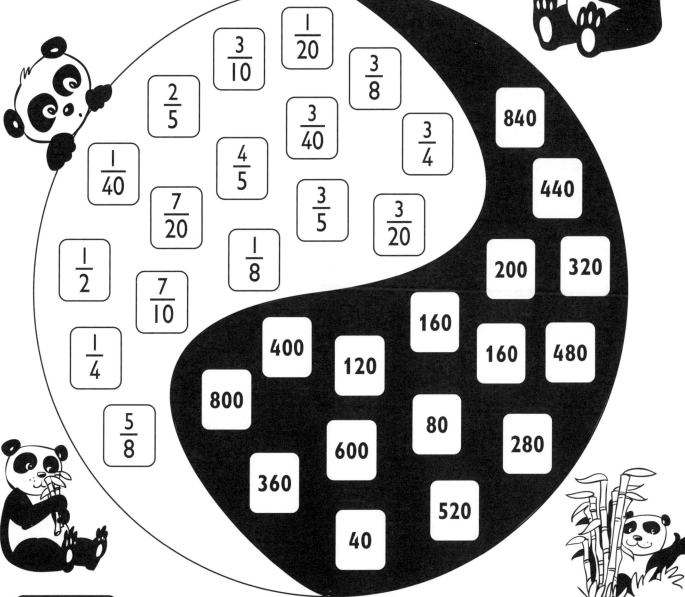

NOW TRY THIS!

• Which fraction and number produce the highest score?

Teachers' note If preferred, the children could use counters. Encourage them to use mental methods to work out each answer, for example dividing by the denominator first to find, say one-eighth, and then multiplying by the numerator to find several, say five-eighths.

A Lesson for Every Day
Maths
10-11 Years
© A&C Black

Hens and chicks

There are ⬚2⬚ chicks to ⬚7⬚ hens in the farmyard.

- Use the diagram to help you answer the questions.

1 How many chicks are in the yard if there are:

a 12 hens? _____

b 4 hens? _____

c 18 hens? _____

d 26 hens? _____

e 30 hens? _____

f 22 hens? _____

2 How many hens are in the yard if there are:

a 21 chicks? _____

b 35 chicks? _____

c 49 chicks? _____

d 28 chicks? _____

e 56 chicks? _____

f 84 chicks? _____

NOW TRY THIS!

- **How many hens and chicks are in the yard if there are:**

a 36 birds?   **b** 54 birds?   **c** 108 birds?

_____ hens   _____ hens   _____ hens

_____ chicks   _____ chicks   _____ chicks

Teachers' note A ratio diagram helps children to understand scaling up or down in a given ratio. Demonstrate how the diagram can be used to find the given number of hens, chicks or birds. When this has been found, the corresponding number of hens or chicks can be identified.

A Lesson for Every Day
Maths
10–11 Years
© A&C Black

'Coven' Garden Market

☆ Cut out the cards.

☆ Pick a large card and a small card.

☆ Work out the calculation and record it on paper.

2 spider webs cost 60p 	4 hairy moles cost 88p 	3 maggoty apples cost 90p 
5 phials of venom cost £10 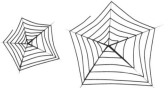	6 boxes of dandruff flakes cost £6.60 	2 snail shells cost £1.20 
5 toad warts cost £1.25 	3 owl pellets cost 93p 	6 jars of slug slime cost £18 
2 plugs of earwax cost £1.80 	4 pots of spots cost £5 	2 balls of bellybutton fluff cost £1.60 
4 bags of bat droppings cost £2.40 	3 tubs of toenail clippings cost £6.90 	5 bottles of cat spit cost £6 

Find the cost of one.	Find the cost of two.	Find the cost of three.	Find the cost of four.
Find the cost of five.	Find the cost of six.	Find the cost of seven.	Find the cost of eight.
Find the cost of nine.	Find the cost of ten.	Find the cost of eleven.	Find the cost of twelve.

Teachers' note Explain to the children that if they draw two cards with the same number of items, they should replace one of them and pick a new card. Encourage the children to work out how much one item costs first, before working out the new quantity.

A Lesson for Every Day
Maths
10–11 Years
© A&C Black

Eggs-ibition

A modern artist has made an exhibition of eggs in boxes. It shows different ways of putting two eggs, one white and one brown, in an egg box.

- Draw eggs in as many different ways as you can.

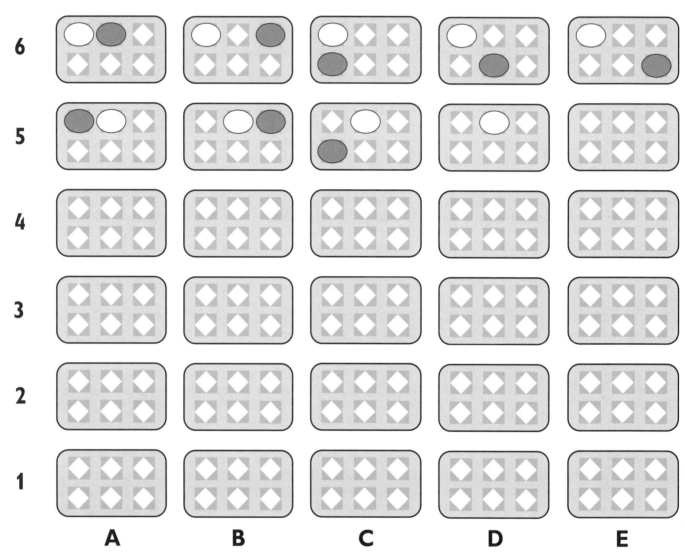

	A	B	C	D	E

(Rows labelled 6, 5, 4, 3, 2, 1 from top to bottom)

- Organise and group your solutions and say how many different 'distinct' solutions there are.

Talk to a partner about any patterns you notice.

- Choose and draw six solutions to show the class.
- Explain to the class why you chose them.

Teachers' note Encourage the children to work systematically and to compare and discuss their solutions. Ask them to identify which are rotations or reflections of others when organising their solutions into groups. The children could describe solutions using the letters and numbers of the grid, or they could cut out the pieces and move them around.

A Lesson for Every Day
Maths
10-11 Years
© A&C Black

Puzzle patterns

- **Solve each problem and show the calculation that you used.**

Work with a partner.

---

1 Alfie and Billy pour 20 buckets of water into a trough. Alfie's bucket holds 10 litres and Billy's holds 7 litres.

The amount of water in the trough is 176 litres.

How many buckets of water each, did Alfie and Billy pour into the trough?

---

2 Jake has a train with lots of carriages. Some of the carriages are 10 cm in length and some are 6 cm. He puts 15 carriages together in a line.
The line is 1·22 m.

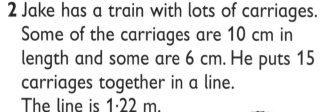

How many carriages are 10 cm long, and how many are 6 cm?

---

3 There are 30 tins on a shelf. The large tins weigh 500 g each and the small tins weigh 300 g.

The tins weigh a total of 11 kg.

How many small tins and how many large tins are there?

---

4 There are 40 children on a trip. Some pay £5 for the trip, which includes lunch. Others pay £3 as they take their own packed lunch. The 40 children pay a total of £150.

How many children pay £5, and how many pay £3?

NOW TRY THIS!

- **Now talk to your partner about what you notice about these problems.**

Teachers' note The numbers and prices can be altered to provide differentiation. Provide the children with calculators for this activity. Encourage the children to describe their strategy and/or calculation for working out each answer, including saying whether they used mental methods, written methods, or a calculator.

A Lesson for Every Day
Maths
10-11 Years
© A&C Black

How did you work it out?

- **With a partner, solve each problem and write down how you worked out the answer.**

1 How many days is it from January 5th to December 23rd in the same year?

2 Which two consecutive numbers have a product of 210?

3 A regular hexagon is folded in half. What shape is the half and what are its angles?

4 Which two fractions with a numerator of 1 have a total of $\frac{5}{6}$?

NOW TRY THIS!

- **On the back of this sheet, show how you would solve this problem:**

When rolling two dice, how many different ways are there of getting a total below 8?

Teachers' note The focus of this activity is on explaining how each pair of children would go about solving the problems and showing this clearly enough for someone else to understand. Encourage the children to swap worksheets with others so that they can compare different forms of representation and explanation.

A Lesson for Every Day
Maths
10-11 Years
© A&C Black

Percentage rocket race

- **Play this game with a partner.**

☆ Each player starts with £100.

☆ Take turns to roll the dice and move your counter around the track.

☆ Use your calculator to work out the amount you win or lose. Round your answers to the nearest pence. Keep your own total.

☆ The winner is the first player to reach **£500**.

> **You each need** a calculator, a counter and some scrap paper, and a dice to share.

Win 17% of £53

Lose 21% of £115

Win 94% of £78

Lose 81% of £124

START

Lose 73% of £36

Win 37% of £98

Lose 13% of £325

Win 63% of £104

Win 61% of £145

Win 65% of £116

Win 87% of £85

Lose 28% of £67

Lose 45% of £33

Win 73% of £121

Win 91% of £111

Win 24% of £63

Win 66% of £38

Lose 88% of £97

Win 7% of £489

Win 19% of £276

Win 66% of £75

Lose 2% of £744

Win 44% of £164

Lose 97% of £103

Lose 32% of £116

Lose 58% of £88

Teachers' note Discuss suitable ways of calculating percentages of amounts using a calculator, for example thinking of 15% as $\frac{15}{100}$ or 15 ÷ 100 and multiplying by the number, or by first dividing the number by 100 to find 1% and then multiplying by 15 to find 15%.

A Lesson for Every Day
Maths
10–11 Years
© A&C Black

Extreme sports

- **Use a calculator to help you solve these problems.**

> At a surfing competition £150 000 was given as prize money.
> 75% was given to the winner and 15% to the runner-up.
> The rest was shared between the two other semi-finalists.

1. How much money was won by:

    (a) the winner? £ _____   **(b)** the runner-up? £ _____

2. What fraction of the prize money did the semi-finalists share?   ☐/☐
    Give your answer in its simplest form.

3. How much money did each semi-finalist win? £ _____

> At a canoeing competition, £125 000 was given as prize money.
> 87% was given to the winner and 11% to the runner-up.
> The rest was shared between the two other semi-finalists.

4. How much money was won by:

    (a) the winner? £ _____   **(b)** the runner-up? £ _____
    (c) each semi-finalist? £ _____

> At a snowboarding competition, £275 000 was given as prize money.
> 65% was given to the winner, 21% to second place, 6% to third place,
> 4% to fourth place, 3% to fifth place and the rest to the player in sixth place.

5. How much money was won by the player:

    (a) who won? £ _____   **(b)** in second place? £ _____
    (c) in third place? £ _____   **(d)** in fourth place? £ _____
    (e) in fifth place? £ _____   **(f)** in sixth place? £ _____

6. What fraction of the prize money did the player in fourth place win?   ☐/☐
    Give your answer in its simplest form.

Teachers' note Children should be given calculators for this activity. Encourage them to describe how they worked out each problem and to discuss their strategies with a partner. As an extension, ask the children to make up some prize money questions of their own for a partner to solve.

A Lesson for Every Day
Maths
10–11 Years
© A&C Black

Domino loop

- **Cut along the dotted lines and make a domino loop.**

Play this game with a partner.

$19\frac{1}{2}$	$\frac{14}{3}$	$7\frac{6}{7}$	$\frac{9}{4}$	$2\frac{1}{4}$	$\frac{15}{4}$
$3\frac{3}{4}$	$\frac{13}{8}$	$5\frac{4}{5}$	$\frac{55}{9}$	$4\frac{2}{3}$	$\frac{55}{7}$
$6\frac{1}{9}$	$\frac{30}{7}$	$6\frac{1}{8}$	$\frac{23}{3}$	$1\frac{5}{8}$	$\frac{22}{3}$
$8\frac{1}{2}$	$\frac{34}{5}$	$6\frac{1}{7}$	$\frac{39}{2}$	$7\frac{1}{3}$	$\frac{11}{4}$
$5\frac{1}{3}$	$\frac{39}{4}$	$2\frac{3}{4}$	$\frac{16}{3}$	$6\frac{4}{5}$	$\frac{43}{7}$
$9\frac{3}{4}$	$\frac{50}{9}$	$8\frac{3}{4}$	$\frac{29}{9}$	$2\frac{2}{5}$	$\frac{19}{4}$
$4\frac{2}{7}$	$\frac{49}{8}$	$3\frac{2}{9}$	$\frac{29}{5}$	$7\frac{2}{3}$	$\frac{19}{10}$
$1\frac{9}{10}$	$\frac{17}{2}$	$5\frac{5}{9}$	$\frac{12}{5}$	$4\frac{3}{4}$	$\frac{35}{4}$

Teachers' note When making a loop, the children should convert the mixed number to an improper fraction and place the correct answer to the left of it, or convert the improper fraction to a mixed number and place a domino showing this to the right of it. The children could time how quickly they complete the loop and then repeat, trying to improve their times.

A Lesson for Every Day
Maths
10-11 Years
© A&C Black

Robot twins

- ## Write each fraction in its simplest form.

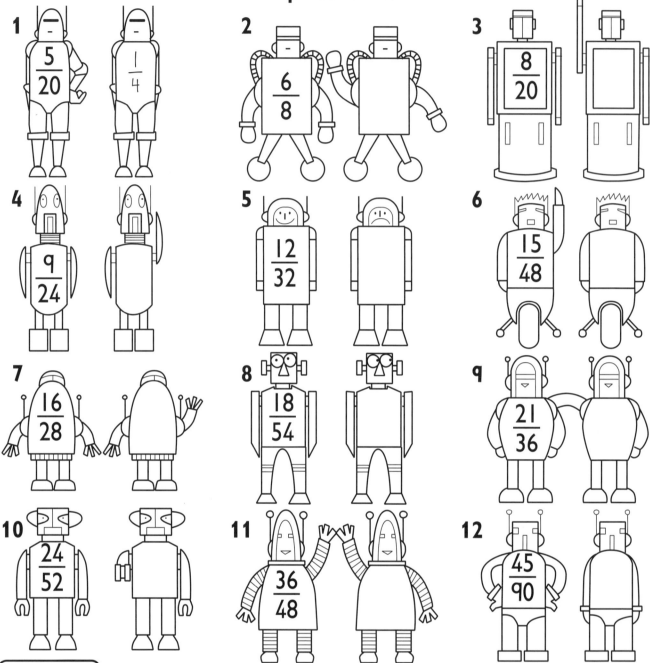

1 $\dfrac{5}{20}$ $\dfrac{1}{4}$

2 $\dfrac{6}{8}$

3 $\dfrac{8}{20}$

4 $\dfrac{9}{24}$

5 $\dfrac{12}{32}$

6 $\dfrac{15}{48}$

7 $\dfrac{16}{28}$

8 $\dfrac{18}{54}$

9 $\dfrac{21}{36}$

10 $\dfrac{24}{52}$

11 $\dfrac{36}{48}$

12 $\dfrac{45}{90}$

NOW TRY THIS!

- ## Use these numbers to make ten different fractions.
- ## Write each fraction in its simplest form.

12	8	48	400	24
	100	50	36	56	300
500	16	20	64	88
	32	200	80	72	320

Teachers' note Remind the children that when simplifying fractions, the numerator and the denominator should be divided by the largest number possible, leaving no remainders.

A Lesson for Every Day
Maths
10–11 Years
© A&C Black

Write each fraction in its simplest form.

1

$\frac{12}{40}$ $\frac{3}{10}$

2

$\frac{45}{75}$

3
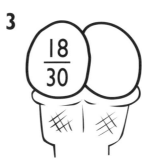
$\frac{18}{30}$

4

$\frac{45}{135}$

5
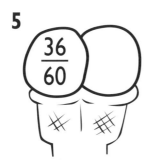
$\frac{36}{60}$

6

$\frac{24}{56}$

7
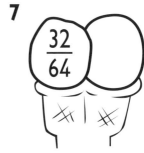
$\frac{32}{64}$

8

$\frac{28}{84}$

9
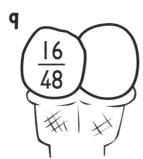
$\frac{16}{48}$

10
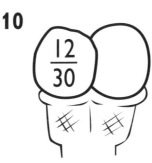
$\frac{12}{30}$

11

$\frac{24}{90}$

12

$\frac{17}{51}$

13
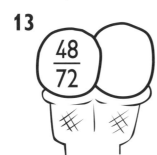
$\frac{48}{72}$

14
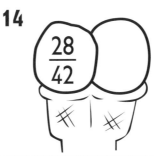
$\frac{28}{42}$

15
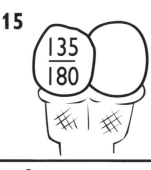
$\frac{135}{180}$

NOW TRY THIS!

• **What fraction of 40 is each number?**
  Give your answer in its simplest form.

10 $\frac{1}{4}$ 4 ____   8 ____   2 ____   5 ____   1 ____

15 ____   16 ____   12 ____   18 ____   25 ____   38 ____

Teachers' note Remind the children that when simplifying fractions, the numerator and the denominator should be divided by the largest number possible, leaving no remainders.

A Lesson for Every Day
Maths
10-11 Years
© A&C Black

Percentage code

- Convert each fraction to an equivalent one with a denominator of 100 and write it as an equivalent percentage.
- Use the key to spell out the name of a fraction.

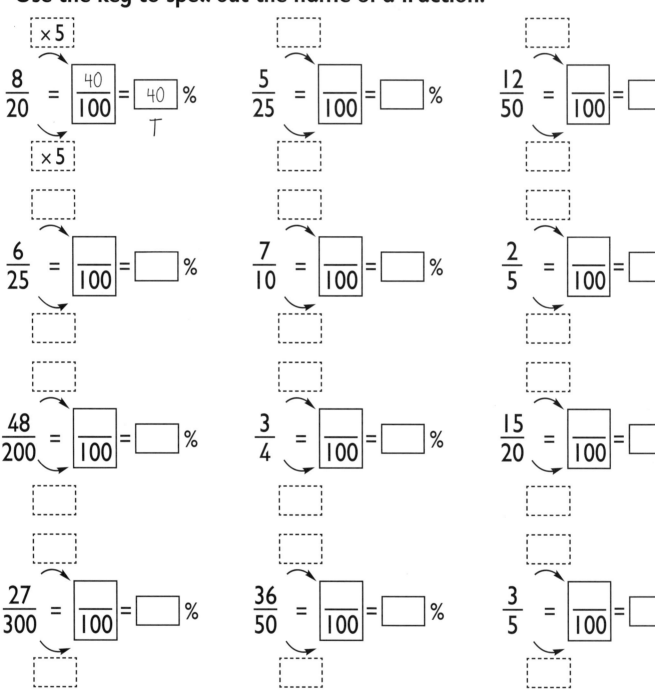

Key

A	35%	E	60%	I	9%	O	24%	U	70%	F	75%
S	22%	T	40%	V	72%	W	20%	L	55%	R	30%

Teachers' note Point out to the children that sometimes they will have to multiply and sometimes divide in order to convert the fractions. Provide the children with a calculator to check their answers and show them that fractions can be converted to percentages by dividing the numerator by the denominator and then multiplying by 100.

A Lesson for Every Day
Maths
10–11 Years
© A&C Black

gBay

On an online shopping site, people selling items (sellers) are scored positively or negatively.

Their 'rating' is the number of positive scores out of the total number of scores, given as a percentage.

• Work out the percentages for each seller.

categories	Seller	Positive scores	Total scores	Percentage rating
	'loads2sell'	42	50	84%
	'moneybags'	8	10	
	'sellagain'	21	25	
	'buynow'	19	20	
	'Davesdeals'	43	50	
	'TVs4u'	4	5	
	'superseller!'	3	4	
	'robme'	18	20	
	'best1'	24	25	
	'me2u'	180	200	
	'The12C'	420	500	
	'££cash££'	870	1000	
	'dodgydan'	90	300	
	'gr8deals'	4500	5000	
	'buyfromme'	360	400	
	'powerseller'	9100	10 000	

search

shop

my gbay

cart

help

NOW TRY THIS!

• **Write five sets of scores that would have a rating of 85%.**

Teachers' note Encourage the children to think of each score as a fraction first, and then to convert the fraction so that it has a denominator of 100 in order to convert it to a percentage. As a check, provide the children with a calculator and show them that fractions can be converted to percentages by dividing the numerator by the denominator and then multiplying by 100.

A Lesson for Every Day
Maths
10-11 Years
© A&C Black

Cat and mouse

- ## Play this game with a partner.

☆ Decide who is the cat and who is the mouse. Then place your counters on the starting positions.

☆ The mouse goes first, moving one space in any direction to a touching square. It can then jump to any space that shows an equivalent amount to the square it has landed on.

☆ The cat moves next, in the same way. The aim for the cat is to jump on the mouse. The aim for the mouse is to escape the cat!

☆ If the mouse survives for 20 moves, it wins. If not, the cat wins.

You need a different coloured counter each.

$\frac{1}{3}$	$\frac{1}{10}$	40%	0·6	$\frac{3}{4}$	**start**
$\frac{1}{5}$	7%	$\frac{53}{100}$	$\frac{1}{2}$	20%	0·4
0·5	0·333	0·75	0·53	0·07	0·9
14%	$\frac{3}{5}$	25%	10%	0·666	33·3%
$\frac{7}{50}$	$\frac{2}{5}$	50%	**start**	$\frac{1}{4}$	$\frac{2}{3}$
0·2	0·1	$\frac{7}{100}$	0·25	0·07	0·14
60%	66·6%	$\frac{9}{10}$	90%	75%	53%

Teachers' note Ensure that the children realise that 'any direction' means up or down, sideways or diagonally, Encourage the children to play the game several times, swapping roles. As an extension, invite the children to write all the fractions, decimals and percentages into a three-columned table, showing equivalents in the same row.

A Lesson for Every Day
Maths
10-11 Years
© A&C Black

Book boxes

A library is moving to a new building and all the books are being packed into boxes. The books come in three different sizes:

- **For each set of books, answer these questions:**

Each box holds 4 large books

or 7 medium books

or 9 small books

How many boxes will be full?

328 small books

$328 \div 9 =$ **36** $\dfrac{4}{9}$

What fraction of the next box will be taken up with the remaining books?

1. 328 small books **36** $\dfrac{4}{9}$	**2.** 571 medium books	**3.** 729 large books
4. 762 small books	**5.** 432 medium books	**6.** 351 large books
7. 363 small books	**8.** 548 medium books	**9.** 626 large books
10. 865 small books	**11.** 439 medium books	**12.** 518 large books

NOW TRY THIS!

- **Find the total number of boxes needed by the library to pack up all the books.** _____

$37 + \ldots$

Teachers' note At the start of the lesson, demonstrate how a remainder can be written as a fraction where the denominator is the divisor and the numerator is the remainder. For the extension activity, remind the children that the remainders should be rounded up each time.

A Lesson for Every Day
Maths
10–11 Years
© A&C Black

Quotient quiz

A [quotient] is the answer to a division question.

- **Tick the correct answer for each question.**

		Drew	Alice	Sadie
1.	87 ÷ 5	17·2	17·4 ✓	17·7
2.	89 ÷ 4	22·9	22·1	22·25
3.	76 ÷ 10	7·1	7·6	7·8
4.	99 ÷ 4	24·75	24·4	24·5
5.	63 ÷ 6	10·3	10·5	10·6
6.	98 ÷ 8	12·2	12·25	12·3
7.	93 ÷ 6	15·3	15·0	15·5
8.	99 ÷ 5	19·4	19·8	19·5
9.	74 ÷ 4	18·5	18·4	18·2
10.	86 ÷ 8	10·25	10·5	10·75

- **Who won the quiz?** _____

NOW TRY THIS!

- **Use a calculator to check your answers.**

Teachers' note Revise fractional and decimal equivalents such as $\frac{1}{5} = 0.2$, $\frac{3}{4} = 0.75$ etc. Children can be encouraged first to write the remainder as a fraction of the divisor, for example $37 ÷ 5 = 7\frac{2}{5}$, and then to convert the fraction to a decimal: 7.4.

A Lesson for Every Day
Maths
10–11 Years
© A&C Black

192

Fraction-packed shapes

You need a ruler and a sharp coloured pencil.

• **Draw each new shape inside the shape shown.**

1.

Draw a square with sides that are $\frac{4}{5}$ as long as the sides of this square.

Write the length of the perimeter **or** the length of the sides on your new shapes.

2.

Draw a rectangle whose perimeter is $\frac{3}{4}$ as long as the perimeter of this rectangle.

3.

Draw a rectangle whose perimeter is $\frac{8}{9}$ as long as the perimeter of this rectangle.

4.

Draw a rectangle whose perimeter is $\frac{3}{5}$ as long as the perimeter of this rectangle.

5.

Draw a rectangle whose width is $\frac{3}{5}$ as long as this width and whose length is $\frac{2}{3}$ as long as this length.

width

length

NOW TRY THIS!

• **You need a pair of compasses.**

☆ On a piece of paper, draw a circle with a diameter of 20 cm.

☆ Inside it draw a circle whose diameter is $\frac{4}{5}$ as large.

☆ Inside that draw a circle whose diameter is $\frac{3}{4}$ as large as the smaller circle.

Teachers' note The children can be given calculators to help them find the fraction of each length. Encourage them to divide the length by the denominator and multiply by the numerator. Explain that this can be done in any order, for example $\frac{2}{5}$ of 5.5 = 5.5 ÷ 5 × 2 = 5.5 × 2 ÷ 5 = 2 ÷ 5 × 5.5.

A Lesson for Every Day
Maths
10–11 Years
© A&C Black

Percentage strip

☆ Cut out both strips and glue them together to make a 0–100 percentage strip.

☆ Choose an amount to write into the 100% box from the selection below.

£3 £6 £9
£8
£12 £7
£4

☆ Now fill in the other boxes, starting with the shaded ones, to show percentages of that amount.

Talk to a partner about how you worked out the answers.

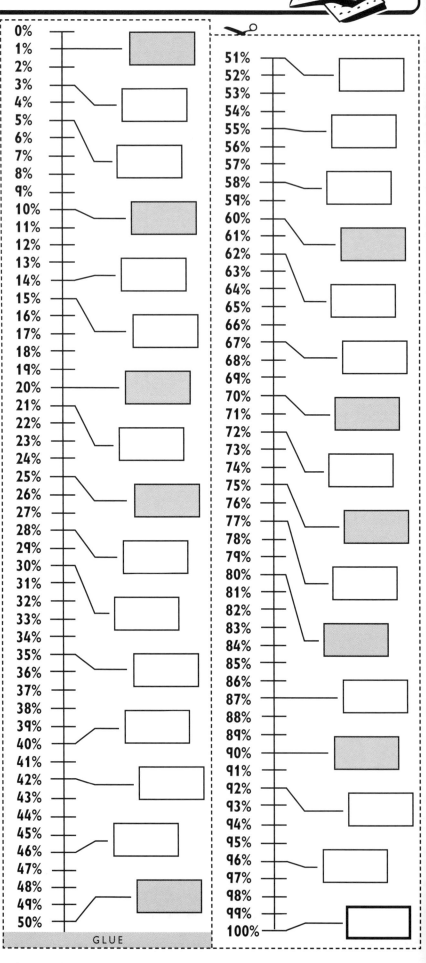

A Lesson for Every Day
Maths
10–11 Years
© A&C Black

Teachers' note This activity can help children to understand the nature of percentages and to develop mental methods that help them to calculate percentages of amounts. Discuss how 50%, 25%, 10% and 1% of a number can be found and how the answers can be used to find other percentages mentally. Some children could be given calculators to help them with this activity.

Great grams

Flour
Price per 100 g: 60p

Sugar
Price per 100 g: 80p

Oats
Price per 100 g: £1.20

Butter
Price per 100 g: £1.10

- **Answer these proportion questions, using the information on the food labels.**

1 How much would Liam pay for:

a 300 g of flour? _____   **b** 200 g of sugar? _____

c 50 g of oats? _____   **d** 50 g of butter? _____

e 150 g of flour? _____   **f** 250 g of sugar? _____

g 450 g of oats? _____   **h** 350 g of butter? _____

i 750 g of flour? _____   **j** 950 g of sugar? _____

k 125 g of oats? _____   **l** 650 g of butter? _____

2 How many grams did Katie buy, if she spent:

a £2.40 on flour? _____ g   **b** £2.40 on sugar? _____ g

c £2.40 on oats? _____ g   **d** £3.30 on butter? _____ g

e £1.50 on flour? _____ g   **f** £2 on sugar? _____ g

g £2.70 on oats? _____ g   **h** £11 on butter? _____ g

i 75p on flour? _____ g   **j** £1.40 on sugar? _____ g

k £3.90 on oats? _____ g   **l** £4.95 on butter? _____ g

NOW TRY THIS!

- **How much is each item** | per gram | **?**

   flour ____ p   sugar ____ p   oats ____ p   butter ____ p

Teachers' note Encourage the children to describe their own methods for working out these proportions. Discuss effective methods and encourage the children to try each others' approaches. The prices can be masked and altered before the sheet is copied for further practice.

A Lesson for Every Day
Maths
10-11 Years
© A&C Black

A matter of balance: 1

- Each set of balance scales holds some kilogram weights and a parcel.
- Work out the mass of each parcel.
- Show your working.

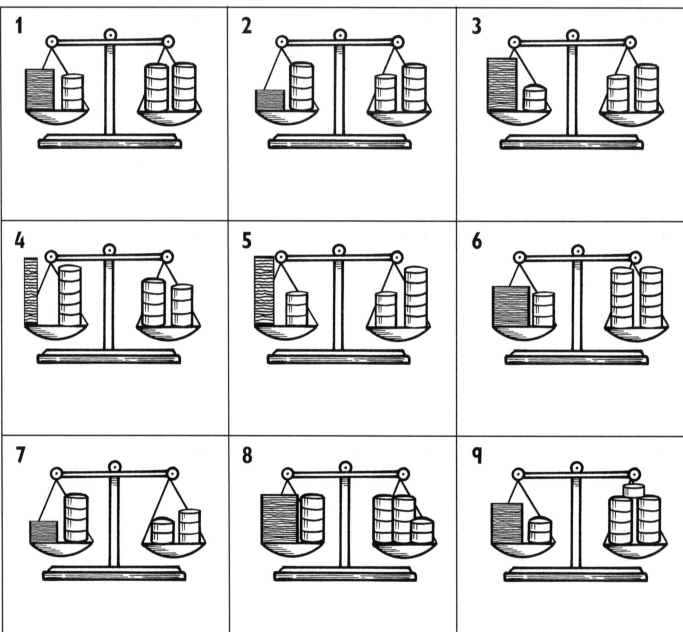

1

2

3

4

5

6

7

8

9

NOW TRY THIS!

- Write a set of instructions to explain to someone else how to answer each problem.

Teachers' note The children could be asked to write an equation for each situation, using a letter, symbol or picture to represent the mass of the parcel, for example $m + 3 = 8$. Discuss that, for this situation, if 3 kg was subtracted from each side of the scales, then the value of m could be found: $m + 3 - 3 = 8 - 3$, therefore m must equal 5.

A Lesson for Every Day
Maths
10–11 Years
© A&C Black

- **Each set of balance scales holds some kilogram weights and some identical parcels.**
- **Work out the mass of each parcel.**
- **Show your working.**

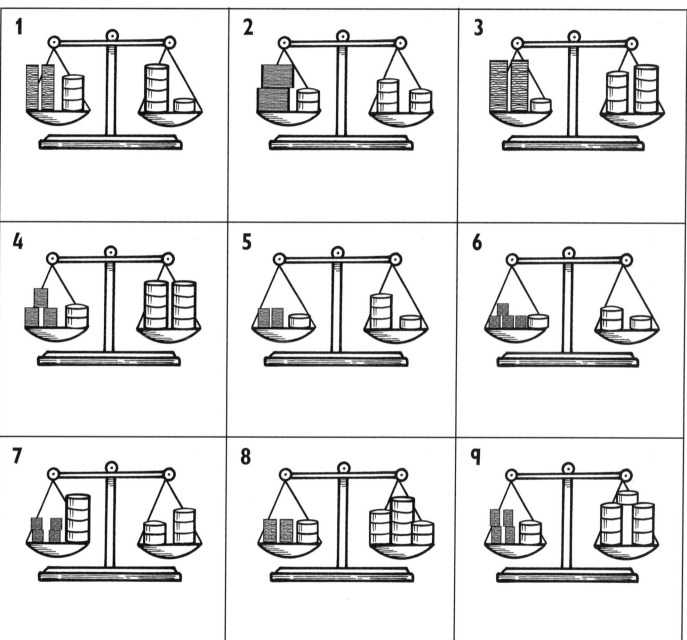

1

2

3

4

5

6

7

8

9

NOW TRY THIS!

- **Write a set of instructions to explain to someone else how to answer each problem.**

Teachers' note The children could be asked to write an equation for each situation, using a letter, symbol or picture to represent the mass of the parcel, for example 2m + 3 = 5. Discuss that, for this situation, if 3 kg was subtracted from each side of the scales, then the value of 2m could be found: 2m + 3 − 3 = 5 − 3, therefore 2m must equal 2 and m must equal 1.

A Lesson for Every Day
Maths
10–11 Years
© A&C Black

Gas bill changes

The cost of a gas bill is changing. The prices are being increased by 10% and then reduced by 10%.

- **Will the bills be the same or different after both changes?**
- **Work out the final bills for these amounts.**

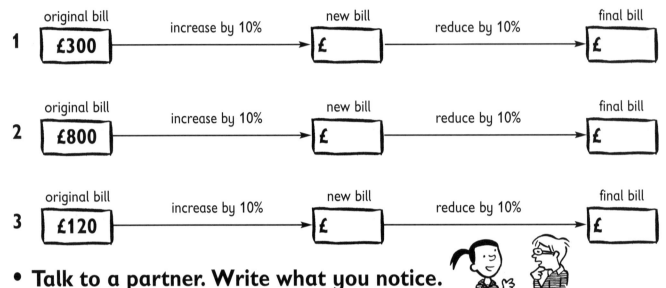

1

original bill | increase by 10% | new bill | reduce by 10% | final bill
£300 | | £ | | £

2

original bill | increase by 10% | new bill | reduce by 10% | final bill
£800 | | £ | | £

3

original bill | increase by 10% | new bill | reduce by 10% | final bill
£120 | | £ | | £

- **Talk to a partner. Write what you notice.**

_____

_____

NOW TRY THIS!

- **Does it make a difference to the final bill if the original price is increased first or reduced first?**

original bill | increase by 10% | new bill | reduce by 10% | final bill
£500 | | £ | | £

original bill | reduce by 10% | new bill | increase by 10% | final bill
£500 | | £ | | £

- **Talk to a partner. Write what you notice.**

_____

_____

Teachers' note It is important that the children understand that the second increase (or decrease) is of the new amount and not the original amount. Encourage the children to explain why there is a difference, and to investigate these ideas further in their own way. Provide the children with calculators for this activity.

A Lesson for Every Day
Maths
10–11 Years
© A&C Black

'Expert' deals

The local 'Expert' shop is offering:

* ✱ 5% discount if you pay with cash

* ✱ 10% discount if you have bought something else from the shop in the last month

* ✱ an <u>extra</u> 20% off during the sale.

• **To save the most money, in which order should you use the discounts?**

All three discounts can be used at the same time.

T V

£400

Laptop

£500

Hi-fi

£600

DVD player

£300

NOW TRY THIS!

• **What is the best price for each item?**
• **How much would you save on each item?**

Teachers' note Ensure that the children understand what the problem is about, and that they appreciate that the order of the discounts may affect the final price. Encourage them to select an item and work out its price, given different discount offers. The children should show their workings in the box. For the extension, they should record on a separate piece of paper.

Courgette croquettes

Here is a recipe for making 25 croquettes.

[ ] g courgettes

[ ] g onions

[ ] g feta cheese

[ ] g potatoes

200 g breadcrumbs

[ ] g flour   plus 2 large eggs

- **Use the clues below to help you work out how much of each ingredient is needed for 25 croquettes.**

Clues

 The mass of breadcrumbs needed is one-fifth of the mass of the courgettes.

 When the courgettes and onions are mixed together, the proportion of the mix that is courgette is four-fifths.

 The ratio of onions to feta cheese is 2:1.

 The mass of the breadcrumbs is 40% of the mass of the potatoes.

 The ratio of flour to breadcrumbs is 3:5.

- **Now find the total mass of the ingredients needed.** _____

NOW TRY THIS!

- **Rewrite the recipe, showing how much of each ingredient would be needed to make 35 croquettes.**
- **Explain to a partner how you will work this out.**

200

Teachers' note Provide the children with calculators for this worksheet. Encourage the children to explain how they used the clues to work out the amounts of ingredients, and to identify the calculation they used for each. Also ask them to say whether they found the answers using mental methods (with or without jottings), written methods, or a calculator.

A Lesson for Every Day
Maths
10-11 Years
© A&C Black

Division decisions

- **Cut out the small hexagons and arrange them onto the large hexagons to show the correct answer to each question.**

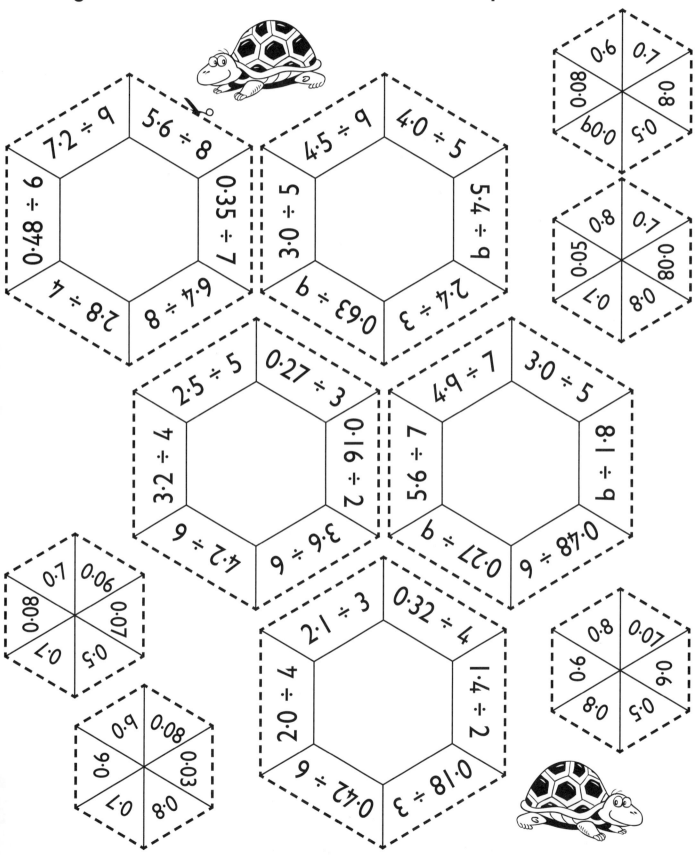

7·2 ÷ 9
5·6 ÷ 8
0·48 ÷ 6
0·35 ÷ 7
2·8 ÷ 4
8 ÷ 7·9

4·5 ÷ 9
4·0 ÷ 5
3·0 ÷ 5
5·4 ÷ 9
3 ÷ 4·2
0·63 ÷ 9

0·6   0·7
0·08   0·8
0·09   0·5

0·8   0·7
0·05   0·08
0·7   0·8

2·5 ÷ 5
0·27 ÷ 3
3·2 ÷ 4
0·16 ÷ 2
4·2 ÷ 6
3·6 ÷ 6

4·9 ÷ 7
3·0 ÷ 5
5·6 ÷ 7
9 ÷ 8·1
0·48 ÷ 6
9 ÷ 0·27

0·7   0·06
0·08   0·07
0·7   0·5

0·9   0·08
0·6   0·03
0·7   0·8

2·1 ÷ 3
0·32 ÷ 4
2·0 ÷ 4
1·4 ÷ 2
0·42 ÷ 6
3 ÷ 0·18

0·8   0·07
0·6   0·6
0·8   0·5

A Lesson for Every Day
Maths
10-11 Years
© A&C Black

Teachers' note Ensure the children understand that there is only one correct position in which each small hexagon can be placed where all the decimals are the correct answers to the questions. Some children might find it easier to answer each question first, writing the answers in the centre of the large hexagons before placing the smaller ones on top of their answers.

201

Precision division

- **Partition the number being divided into parts so that one part is the largest multiple of 10 that is divisible by the divisor.**
- **Then complete the calculation.**

1. $5 \overline{)395}$ $= 5 \overline{)350 + \quad 45}$ $= \underline{\quad 70 + 9 \quad}$ $= \underline{\quad 79 \quad}$

2. $6 \overline{)312}$ $= 6 \overline{)300 +\quad}$ $= \underline{\qquad}$ $= \underline{\qquad}$

3. $4 \overline{)256}$ $= 4 \overline{)\qquad}$ $= \underline{\qquad}$ $= \underline{\qquad}$

4. $3 \overline{)159}$ $= 3 \overline{)\qquad}$ $= \underline{\qquad}$ $= \underline{\qquad}$

5. $8 \overline{)736}$ $= 8 \overline{)\qquad}$ $= \underline{\qquad}$ $= \underline{\qquad}$

6. $7 \overline{)189}$ $= 7 \overline{)\qquad}$ $= \underline{\qquad}$ $= \underline{\qquad}$

7. $4 \overline{)236}$ $= 4 \overline{)\qquad}$ $= \underline{\qquad}$ $= \underline{\qquad}$

8. $9 \overline{)585}$ $= 9 \overline{)\qquad}$ $= \underline{\qquad}$ $= \underline{\qquad}$

9. $6 \overline{)384}$ $= 6 \overline{)\qquad}$ $= \underline{\qquad}$ $= \underline{\qquad}$

10. $7 \overline{)504}$ $= 7 \overline{)\qquad}$ $= \underline{\qquad}$ $= \underline{\qquad}$

NOW TRY THIS!

- **Answer these questions, using carrying if you can.**

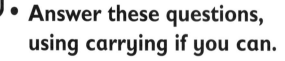

(a) $5 \overline{)3\,9\,^45}$ **(b)** $6 \overline{)3\,9\,6}$ **(c)** $8 \overline{)2\,7\,2}$

(d) $4 \overline{)1\,9\,6}$ **(e)** $7 \overline{)4\,0\,6}$ **(f)** $9 \overline{)7\,0\,2}$

Teachers' note This method of division can lead on to the common short division method and helps children to appreciate the need to partition the number into a multiple of 10 that is divisible by the divisor. For the extension activity, demonstrate how the 4 tens that remain after dividing 39 tens by 5 can be carried across, leaving 45 to be divided by 5.

A Lesson for Every Day
Maths
10–11 Years
© A&C Black

Division patterns

• **Complete these division patterns.**

Notice what happens to the answers if the first number is made **10 times smaller** or **10 times larger**.

$4 \cdot 8 \div 8 = \underline{0.6}$ ⟨ $48 \div 8 = 6$ ⟩ $480 \div 8 = \underline{60}$

$11 \cdot 4 \div 6 = \underline{}$ ⟨ $114 \div 6 = 19$ ⟩ $1140 \div 6 = \underline{}$

$19 \cdot 6 \div 7 = \underline{}$ ⟨ $196 \div 7 = 28$ ⟩ $1960 \div 7 = \underline{}$

$51 \cdot 3 \div 9 = \underline{}$ ⟨ $513 \div 9 = 57$ ⟩ $5130 \div 9 = \underline{}$

• **Use written methods to answer the divisions in the middle.**

Use scrap paper.

• **Then, using the pattern, fill in the other answers.**

$28 \cdot 5 \div 5 = \underline{}$ ⟨ $285 \div 5 = \underline{}$ ⟩ $2850 \div 5 = \underline{}$

$61 \cdot 2 \div 4 = \underline{}$ ⟨ $612 \div 4 = \underline{}$ ⟩ $6120 \div 4 = \underline{}$

$51 \cdot 3 \div 9 = \underline{}$ ⟨ $513 \div 9 = \underline{}$ ⟩ $5130 \div 9 = \underline{}$

$61 \cdot 6 \div 8 = \underline{}$ ⟨ $616 \div 8 = \underline{}$ ⟩ $6160 \div 8 = \underline{}$

$76 \cdot 2 \div 6 = \underline{}$ ⟨ $762 \div 6 = \underline{}$ ⟩ $7620 \div 6 = \underline{}$

NOW TRY THIS!

• **Use your last three answers to answer these.**

$5 \cdot 13 \div 9 = \underline{}$ $6 \cdot 16 \div 8 = \underline{}$ $7 \cdot 62 \div 6 = \underline{}$

Teachers' note As children gain confidence in working with written methods of division they can be introduced to dividing decimals by whole numbers. The children should be encouraged to work out the answer without the decimal points first, and then make the suitable adjustment for the decimal. Encourage them to estimate the size of the answer each time.

A Lesson for Every Day
Maths
10–11 Years
© A&C Black

Soiled goods

- Use a calculator to work out the sale price of each item.
- Round your answers to the nearest pence.

1.

sweat marks

Was £26.50
64% off!

Sale price:

2.

scratched

Were £42.99
38% off!

Sale price:

3.

wheels missing

Were £64
78% off!

Sale price:

4.

a bit stale

Was £0.85
11% off!

Sale price:

5.

won't stay up

Was £7.29
43% off!

Sale price:

6.

a bit cheesy

Were £34.49
27% off!

Sale price:

7.

cracked

Was £3.70
82% off!

Sale price:

8.

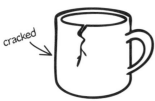

slightly soggy

CRISPS

Were £0.76
47% off!

Sale price:

9.

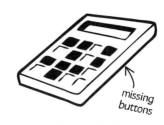

missing buttons

Was £64
69% off!

Sale price:

NOW TRY THIS!

- If you bought all the items, how much would you save in total? _____

Teachers' note The children should be given calculators for this activity. Encourage them to describe how they worked out each problem and to discuss their strategies with a partner.

A Lesson for Every Day
Maths
10–11 Years
© A&C Black

Fraction line-up

- **Change each fraction so that it has the** | common denominator |
  shown on the number line. Join the fraction to the line.

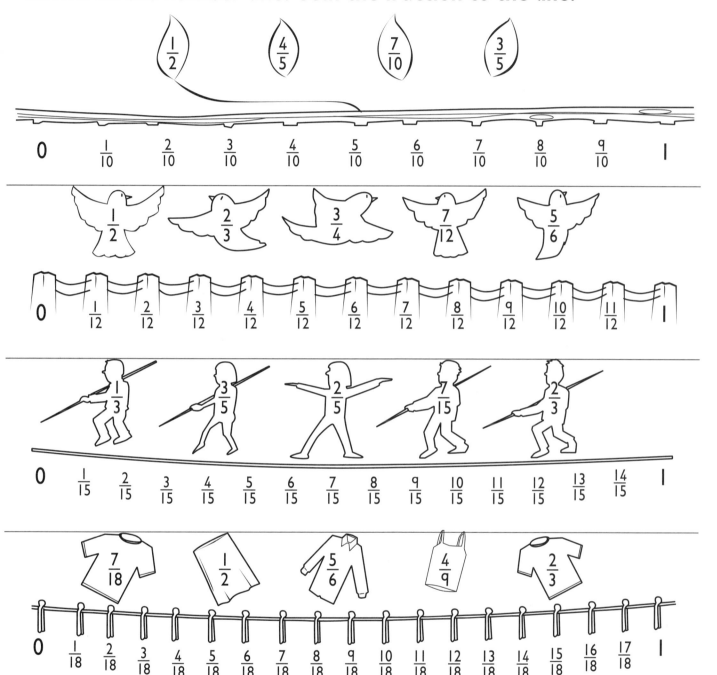

$\frac{1}{2}$ $\frac{4}{5}$ $\frac{7}{10}$ $\frac{3}{5}$

0   $\frac{1}{10}$ $\frac{2}{10}$ $\frac{3}{10}$ $\frac{4}{10}$ $\frac{5}{10}$ $\frac{6}{10}$ $\frac{7}{10}$ $\frac{8}{10}$ $\frac{9}{10}$ 1

$\frac{1}{2}$ $\frac{2}{3}$ $\frac{3}{4}$ $\frac{7}{12}$ $\frac{5}{6}$

0   $\frac{1}{12}$ $\frac{2}{12}$ $\frac{3}{12}$ $\frac{4}{12}$ $\frac{5}{12}$ $\frac{6}{12}$ $\frac{7}{12}$ $\frac{8}{12}$ $\frac{9}{12}$ $\frac{10}{12}$ $\frac{11}{12}$ 1

$\frac{1}{3}$ $\frac{3}{5}$ $\frac{2}{5}$ $\frac{7}{15}$ $\frac{2}{3}$

0   $\frac{1}{15}$ $\frac{2}{15}$ $\frac{3}{15}$ $\frac{4}{15}$ $\frac{5}{15}$ $\frac{6}{15}$ $\frac{7}{15}$ $\frac{8}{15}$ $\frac{9}{15}$ $\frac{10}{15}$ $\frac{11}{15}$ $\frac{12}{15}$ $\frac{13}{15}$ $\frac{14}{15}$ 1

$\frac{7}{18}$ $\frac{1}{2}$ $\frac{5}{6}$ $\frac{4}{9}$ $\frac{2}{3}$

0   $\frac{1}{18}$ $\frac{2}{18}$ $\frac{3}{18}$ $\frac{4}{18}$ $\frac{5}{18}$ $\frac{6}{18}$ $\frac{7}{18}$ $\frac{8}{18}$ $\frac{9}{18}$ $\frac{10}{18}$ $\frac{11}{18}$ $\frac{12}{18}$ $\frac{13}{18}$ $\frac{14}{18}$ $\frac{15}{18}$ $\frac{16}{18}$ $\frac{17}{18}$ 1

NOW TRY THIS!

- **On squared paper, draw a number line from 0 to 1, split into twenty-fourths. Mark on these fractions:**

  $\frac{1}{6}$ $\frac{5}{12}$ $\frac{3}{4}$ $\frac{1}{2}$ $\frac{2}{3}$ $\frac{5}{8}$ $\frac{17}{24}$

Teachers' note Point out to the children that not every fraction will need to be changed to an equivalent one as some will already have the new denominator.

A Lesson for Every Day
Maths
10-11 Years
© A&C Black

Fraction spell

- **Change each fraction to an equivalent one so that all five fractions have a common denominator.**
- **Order the fractions, smallest to largest, to spell a word.**

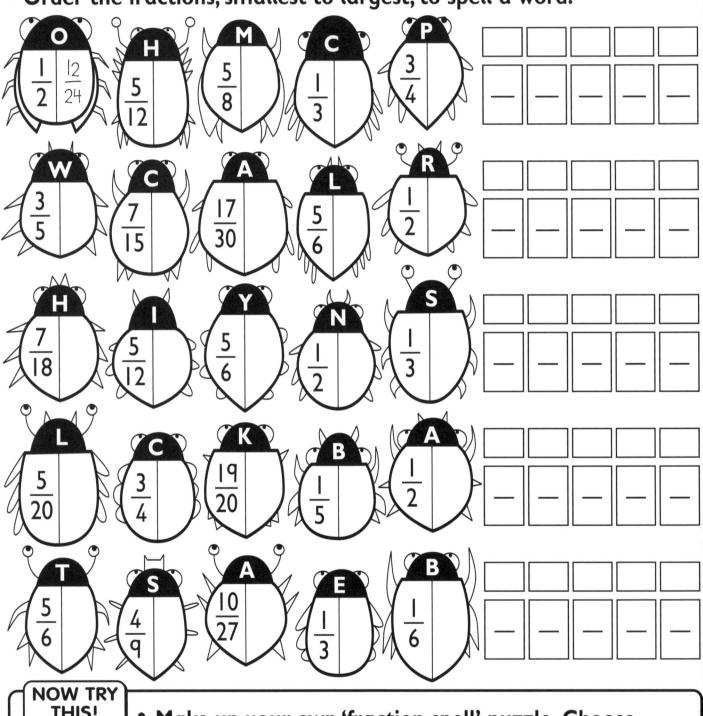

O	H	M	C	P
$\frac{1}{2}$ $\frac{12}{24}$	$\frac{5}{12}$	$\frac{5}{8}$	$\frac{1}{3}$	$\frac{3}{4}$

☐ ☐ ☐ ☐ ☐
__ __ __ __ __

W	C	A	L	R
$\frac{3}{5}$	$\frac{7}{15}$	$\frac{17}{30}$	$\frac{5}{6}$	$\frac{1}{2}$

☐ ☐ ☐ ☐ ☐
__ __ __ __ __

H	I	Y	N	S
$\frac{7}{18}$	$\frac{5}{12}$	$\frac{5}{6}$	$\frac{1}{2}$	$\frac{1}{3}$

☐ ☐ ☐ ☐ ☐
__ __ __ __ __

L	C	K	B	A
$\frac{5}{20}$	$\frac{3}{4}$	$\frac{19}{20}$	$\frac{1}{5}$	$\frac{1}{2}$

☐ ☐ ☐ ☐ ☐
__ __ __ __ __

T	S	A	E	B
$\frac{5}{6}$	$\frac{4}{9}$	$\frac{10}{27}$	$\frac{1}{3}$	$\frac{1}{6}$

☐ ☐ ☐ ☐ ☐
__ __ __ __ __

NOW TRY THIS!

- **Make up your own 'fraction spell' puzzle. Choose fractions that can all be changed to equivalent ones with a common denominator of 36.**

Teachers' note When the children are making up their own puzzles, encourage them to begin with a five-letter word, for example SPEAR or HOUSE, and then to allocate a fraction for each letter, in order. They should then copy out the fractions, with their corresponding letters, in a jumbled order for their partner to solve. These puzzles can form a stimulating classroom display.

A Lesson for Every Day
Maths
10–11 Years
© A&C Black

Telly addict

This TV guide shows the lengths of some programmes, written in fractions of an hour.

- **How long will each programme be in minutes?**

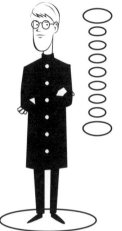

Convert each fraction to an equivalent one with a denominator of 60 to help you.

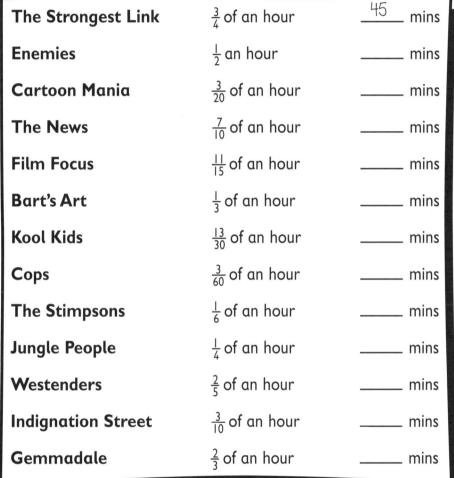

The Strongest Link	$\frac{3}{4}$ of an hour	45 mins
Enemies	$\frac{1}{2}$ an hour	____ mins
Cartoon Mania	$\frac{3}{20}$ of an hour	____ mins
The News	$\frac{7}{10}$ of an hour	____ mins
Film Focus	$\frac{11}{15}$ of an hour	____ mins
Bart's Art	$\frac{1}{3}$ of an hour	____ mins
Kool Kids	$\frac{13}{30}$ of an hour	____ mins
Cops	$\frac{3}{60}$ of an hour	____ mins
The Stimpsons	$\frac{1}{6}$ of an hour	____ mins
Jungle People	$\frac{1}{4}$ of an hour	____ mins
Westenders	$\frac{2}{5}$ of an hour	____ mins
Indignation Street	$\frac{3}{10}$ of an hour	____ mins
Gemmadale	$\frac{2}{3}$ of an hour	____ mins

- **Write each fraction in order. Start with the shortest programme.**

NOW TRY THIS!

- **Put these fractions of a day in order, starting with the smallest.**

$\frac{3}{4}$ $\frac{1}{6}$ $\frac{5}{8}$ $\frac{11}{12}$ $\frac{2}{3}$ $\frac{1}{2}$ $\frac{7}{24}$ $\frac{5}{6}$

Convert each fraction to an equivalent one with a denominator of 24 to help you.

Teachers' note Remind the children that, when finding equivalent fractions, both the numerator and the denominator must be multiplied or divided by the same number. Here, children should look at the existing denominator and decide what it must be multiplied by to make 60. They should then multiply the numerator by that number.

A Lesson for Every Day
Maths
10–11 Years
© A&C Black

Hoopla stall

- **Ring the fractions that are equivalent to each percentage.**

> More than one fraction can be ringed.

40% $\left(\dfrac{2}{5}\right)$ $\dfrac{8}{10}$ $\dfrac{40}{60}$ $\dfrac{40}{100}$ $\dfrac{5}{8}$ $\dfrac{4}{10}$

60% $\dfrac{3}{5}$ $\dfrac{30}{50}$ $\dfrac{6}{10}$ $\dfrac{19}{3}$ $\dfrac{60}{100}$ $\dfrac{3}{6}$

75% $\dfrac{18}{24}$ $\dfrac{3}{4}$ $\dfrac{12}{16}$ $\dfrac{9}{12}$ $\dfrac{6}{8}$ $\dfrac{8}{12}$

15% $\dfrac{15}{30}$ $\dfrac{7}{50}$ $\dfrac{15}{100}$ $\dfrac{3}{50}$ $\dfrac{3}{20}$ $\dfrac{1}{15}$

90% $\dfrac{9}{10}$ $\dfrac{90}{10}$ $\dfrac{18}{20}$ $\dfrac{90}{100}$ $\dfrac{10}{9}$ $\dfrac{45}{50}$

25% $\dfrac{1}{4}$ $\dfrac{5}{20}$ $\dfrac{15}{60}$ $\dfrac{8}{32}$ $\dfrac{25}{100}$ $\dfrac{4}{24}$

35% $\dfrac{7}{20}$ $\dfrac{35}{10}$ $\dfrac{35}{100}$ $\dfrac{100}{35}$ $\dfrac{3}{5}$ $\dfrac{35}{50}$

64% $\dfrac{32}{50}$ $\dfrac{64}{10}$ $\dfrac{128}{200}$ $\dfrac{16}{25}$ $\dfrac{64}{100}$ $\dfrac{8}{13}$

NOW TRY THIS!

- **Write six different fractions that are equivalent to 80%.**

Teachers' note This type of question occurs in National Test papers and involves children (a) understanding how percentages can be converted into fractions, and (b) appreciating that there are many equivalent fractions for each percentage.

A Lesson for Every Day
Maths
10–11 Years
© A&C Black

Colour it!

- **Count the number of small shapes in each pattern.**
- **Colour the correct percentage of each shape.**

1

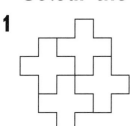

Colour 75% blue.

2

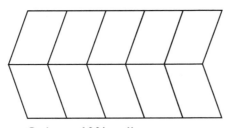

Colour 40% yellow and 10% red.

3

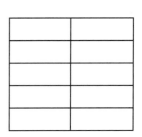

Colour 70% green and 20% blue.

4

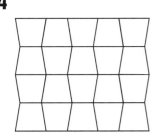

Colour 30% yellow, 15% red and 20% green.

5

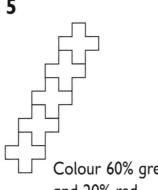

Colour 60% green and 20% red.

6

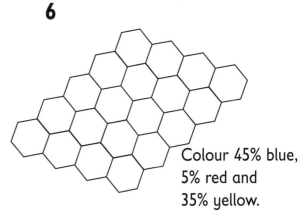

Colour 45% blue, 5% red and 35% yellow.

7

Colour 8% blue, 24% red and 40% yellow.

8

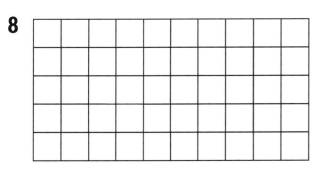

Colour 22% red, 48% yellow and 2% blue.

9

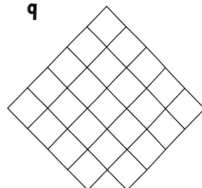

Colour 4% green, 16% yellow and 28% red.

NOW TRY THIS!

- **Calculate the percentage of each shape that is <u>not</u> coloured. Write this percentage next to the shape.**

Teachers' note Demonstrate how to (a) write each percentage as a fraction with a denominator of 100, and (b) convert the fraction to an equivalent one with a denominator that matches the number of small shapes in each pattern. For example in question 9, 4% is written as $\frac{4}{100}$, which converts to $\frac{1}{25}$.

A Lesson for Every Day
Maths
10-11 Years
© A&C Black

Team work

• **Choose the most appropriate answer for each situation.**

1. 26 people are grouped into teams of 6. How many teams and how many people left over?

Work with a partner.

4 r2

2. A piece of string 27cm long is cut into 6 equal pieces. What is the length of each piece in centimetres?

3. Mr Dixon shares £20.25 equally amongst the 5 members of his family. How much does each get?

4. I have 22 photos. I can fit 5 on a page in my album. How many pages will have photos on?

5. 3 sacks of potatoes weigh a total of 13·5 kg. What is the mass in kilograms of each sack of potatoes?

6. A piece of ribbon 34 cm long is cut into 8 cm long pieces. How many 8 cm pieces can be cut?

7. 18 children go on a school trip. If 4 children can fit in each car, how many cars are needed?

8. Kerry has £45 to spend on cinema tickets. She buys 10, leaving no change. How much is each ticket?

9. Pete puts 18 coins into 4 equal piles. How many are in each pile and how many are left over?

10. A doctor has to see 36 patients If he can see 8 patients per hour, how many hours will this take him?

(4·5)

(4)

(4 r2)

(£4.50)

(5)

(4 ½)

(£4.05)

NOW TRY THIS!

• **Write a division problem to which the most appropriate answer would be:**

(6·4)

Teachers' note Encourage the children to discuss whether the answer should be rounded up or down, or whether the remainder should be written as a whole number, fraction or decimal. Some children may find it easier to do the calculation first and then to make that decision.

A Lesson for Every Day
Maths
10–11 Years
© A&C Black

Percentage race rally

- ## Play this game with a partner.
- ☆ Each player starts with £100.
- ☆ Take turns to roll the dice and move your counter around the track.
- ☆ Work out the amount you win or lose using mental methods. Keep your own total.
- ☆ The winner is the first player to reach **£250**.

> **You each need** a counter and some scrap paper, and a dice to share.

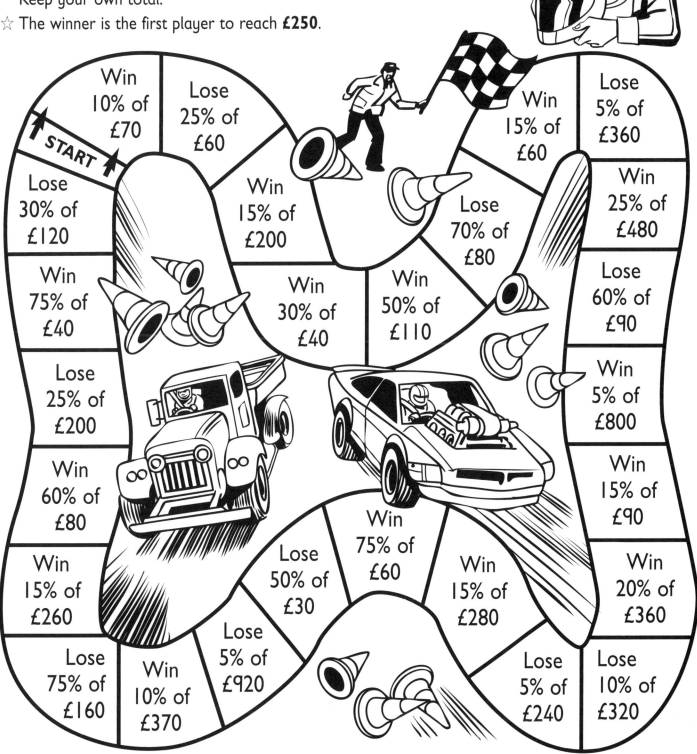

START

Win 10% of £70

Lose 25% of £60

Win 15% of £60

Lose 5% of £360

Lose 30% of £120

Win 15% of £200

Lose 70% of £80

Win 25% of £480

Win 75% of £40

Win 30% of £40

Win 50% of £110

Lose 60% of £90

Lose 25% of £200

Win 5% of £800

Win 60% of £80

Win 15% of £90

Win 15% of £260

Win 75% of £60

Win 15% of £280

Win 20% of £360

Lose 50% of £30

Lose 75% of £160

Win 10% of £370

Lose 5% of £920

Lose 5% of £240

Lose 10% of £320

Teachers' note At the start of the lesson, demonstrate mental methods for finding percentages of whole numbers, for example halving to find 50%, dividing by 10 to find 10% and then using those facts to help find other percentages such as 25%, 20% or 5%. The percentage strip on page 55 could also be used.

A Lesson for Every Day
Maths
10-11 Years
© A&C Black

Are we nearly there?

The Jones family travel from Town **A** to Town **C**,
a distance of **60 km**. They stop on the way at Town **B**.

1 If the distance from A to B is **twice** as far as from B to C,
how far is the distance from A to B? _____ km

A   B   C
|————————————————————————————————————|——————————|
←———————————————— 60 km ————————————————→

2 If the distance from A to B is **three times** as far as from B to C,
how far is the distance from A to B? _____ km

A   B   C
|———————————————————————————————————————|————————|
←———————————————— 60 km ————————————————→

3 If the distance from A to B is **four times** as far as from B to C,
how far is the distance from A to B? _____ km

A   B   C
|——|——————|
←———————————————— 60 km ————————————————→

4 If the distance from A to B is **five times** as far as from B to C,
how far is the distance from A to B? _____ km

A   B   C
|———|—————|
←———————————————— 60 km ————————————————→

5 If the distance from A to B is **nine times** as far as from B to C,
how far is the distance from A to B? _____ km

A   B   C
|——|———|
←———————————————— 60 km ————————————————→

NOW TRY THIS!

- **Imagine that the distance from A to C has changed.
  Answer each question above for these new distances.**
  a 180 km   **b** 90 km

212

Teachers' note This activity provides a useful context for some discussion about proportions. When
the children have completed questions 1 to 5, ask them, in pairs, to discuss how they worked out each
answer. This type of question can be given orally and the children asked to discuss their strategies for
working out the answers.

A Lesson for Every Day
Maths
10–11 Years
© A&C Black

Cooking crisis

More people than expected have arrived at Jamie's restaurant.

- **Help him to rewrite his recipes.**

1

Creamy pea soup for 7 people

175 g butter

210 g peas

350 ml vegetable stock

98 ml double cream

7 tbsp chopped parsley

Creamy pea soup for **9 people**

_____ 225 g butter

_____ g peas

_____ ml vegetable stock

_____ ml double cream

_____ tbsp chopped parsley

2

Beef Baldaire for 3 people

3 garlic cloves

360 g chopped beef

60 ml tomato purée

6 chopped onions

420 g button mushrooms

270 g chopped tomatoes

Beef Baldaire for **8 people**

_____ garlic cloves

_____ g chopped beef

_____ ml tomato purée

_____ chopped onions

_____ g button mushrooms

_____ g chopped tomatoes

3

Marble cake for 4 people

240 g butter

280 g caster sugar

80 g ground almonds

140 g self-raising flour

4 eggs

148 g plain chocolate

Marble cake for **7 people**

_____ g butter

_____ g caster sugar

_____ g ground almonds

_____ g self-raising flour

_____ eggs

_____ g plain chocolate

NOW TRY THIS!

- **Now write how much of each ingredient would be needed to make each recipe for ☐10 people.**

Teachers' note At the start of the lesson, demonstrate how to divide each amount by the number of people stated at the top of the recipe to find how much for one person, and then multiply to find how much for several people.

A Lesson for Every Day
Maths
10-11 Years
© A&C Black

Cheers – page 24

Glasses	Clinks
2	1
3	3
4	6
5	10
6	15
7	21

Now try this!

10	45
11	55
12	66

Mount Everest – page 25
1 a 30°C b 31°C c 29°C d 20°C
2 a 15°C b 21°C c 34°C d 40°C
3 a 14°C b 10°C c 35°C d 31°C
Now try this!
Base Camp 55°C

Fly me to the moon – page 26
1 a 125°C b 180°C c 240°C d 340°C
e 110°C f 0°C g 119°C h 398°C
i 318°C j 277°C
2 a Station 10 b Station 4
3 a 25°C b 20°C c 34°C d 74°C
e 2°C f 44°C g 7°C h 88°C
Now try this!
Stations 1 and 5   Stations 1 and 4
Stations 2 and 6   Stations 4 and 5
Stations 4 and 8   Stations 4 and 10

Totals and products – page 29
1 × 19 = 19   6 × 14 = 84
2 × 18 = 36   7 × 13 = 91
3 × 17 = 51   8 × 12 = 96
4 × 16 = 64   9 × 11 = 99
5 × 15 = 75   10 × 10 = 100
2 74 × 0 = 0   69 × 5 = 345
73 × 1 = 73   68 × 6 = 408
72 × 2 = 144   67 × 7 = 469
71 × 3 = 213   66 × 8 = 528
70 × 4 = 280   65 × 9 = 585

Pesky pets – page 32
Solutions:
1 7 2 9 3 4 4 37 5 14 6 13, 5
7 4.5 8 9.4 9 23 10 5 11 2.9 12 8.9
19

Decimal hops – page 36
Solutions:
11.9 = 6.2 + 3.1 + 0.1 + 0.9 + 1.6
13.5 = 1.3 + 4.6 + 0.1 + 4.2 + 3.3
19.7 = 5.8 + 1.7 + 2.3 + 8.3 + 1.6
18.6 = 3.9 + 2.5 + 5.5 + 4.2 + 0.9 + 1.6
16.2 = 3.9 + 1.9 + 2.7 + 4.4 + 3.3
20.2 = 6.2 + 2.5 + 2.5 + 3.2 + 5.8

Annette's baguettes – page 37
Solutions:
1 £3.82   2 £14.12   3 £10.83
4 62p   5 £1.94   6 £1.23
Now try this!
Solutions include answers between £10.46 and £13.36

Digit discoveries – page 38
1 44.445 2 54.445 3 55.445
4 55.545 5 55.555
Now try this!
(a) 22.233 (b) 32.223 (c) 33.223
(d) 33.323 (e) 33.333

Walter wall carpets – page 39
Solutions:
1 (a) £425 (b) £444 (c) £532 (d) £864
(e) £1248 (f) £1444
2 (f)
Now try this!
(a) 100 m² (b) 148 m² (c) 76 m²
(d) 96 m² (e) 208 m² (f) 304 m²
£4.25   £3   £7
£9   £6   £4.75

Crazy creepy crawlies – page 42
Sample solution:

Calculator errors – page 43
1 George multiplied 40 by 15. (Correct answer = £6)
2 Suzie divided by 3 and multiplied by 8. (Correct answer = 81ml)
3 Martina divided 36 by 12 and then added 4. (Correct answer = 8.32 kg)
4 Asif multiplied 285 by 7 and then added 348. (Correct answer = 4431)

What do you notice? – page 44
1 41 2 5 3 6cm 4 85g

Weighty questions – page 45
2 ≤ k < 4
2.421, 2.425, 2.5, 3, 3.099, 3.4, 3.55
2.789, 2.8, 3.0, 3.725, 3.98, 4.074, 4.462
7.0, 7.567, 7.65, 7.695, 7.765, 7.9, 7.975
8.135, 8.3, 8.315, 8.5, 8.51, 8.513, 8.531
Now try this!
2 ≤ k < 4
2.421, 2.425, 2.5, 3, 3.099, 3.4, 3.55
2.789, 2.8, 3.0, 3.725, 3.98
4 ≤ k < 6
4.074, 4.462
6 ≤ k < 8
7.0, 7.567, 7.65, 7.695, 7.765, 7.9, 7.975
8 ≤ k < 10
8.135, 8.3, 8.315, 8.5, 8.51, 8.513, 8.531

Coconut shy – page 46
0.312 0.337 0.354 0.379 0.393
2.465 2.484 2.508 2.523 2.536
4.81 4.835 4.856 4.88 4.893
6.91 6.938 6.954 6.979 6.993
Now try this!
5.081 5.083 5.086 5.0875 5.0891

On the ball – page 51
1 (a) 14.27 (b) 17.5 (c) 17.36
(d) 16.15 (e) 15.05 (f) 14.08
2 (a) 268.62 (b) 461.42 (c) 22.02
(d) 117.82 (e) 153.22 (f) 56.22

9 to 1 challenge – page 52
There are many different solutions to this challenge. Here are some examples:
98 − 76 + 5432.1 = 5454.1
98.7 + 65.4 − 32.1 = 132
987 + 654 − 321 = 1320
9876 + 54 − 3.21 = 9926.79
9.876 − 5.43 + 2.1 = 6.546
9 − 8.76 + 54.321 = 54.561
9.87 − 6 + 54.321 = 58.191
987 + 654.3 − 321 = 732
9.8 + 76543.2 − 1 = 76552
987.6 × 5.4 − 321 = 672

The mummy's riddle – page 53
94 × 862 = 81 028
Now try this!
9.4 × 8.62 = 81.028

Tile teaser – page 54
Each row, column and diagonal will have two odd numbers and two even numbers. Some arrangements may be alternate odd and even.

Sequence squares – page 55
1 1, 3, 5, 7, 9, 11, 13, 15
2 4, 8, 12, 16, 20, 24, 28, 32
3 2, 4, 6, 8, 10, 12, 14, 16
4 1, 4, 7, 10, 13, 16, 19, 22
5 1, 5, 9, 13, 17, 21, 25, 29

Is it possible? – page 56
1 Yes. Any number whose digits add to make a multiple of 9 must be a multiple of 9, and the total of 7, 5 and 8 is 20, which is not a multiple of 9.

Rounding riddles – page 58
1 True 2 True 3 True 4 True
5 True 6 True 7 False 8 True
9 False 10 False 11 False 12 True

Hidden letters – page 59
SUPERHERO

Inverses in verses – page 60
1 True 2 True 3 False 4 False
5 True 6 True 7 True

Cuboid crazy: 1 and 2 – page 61
Cuboid crazy: 1
1 true 2 false 3 true 4 false
5 true 6 true 7 true 8 true
9 false 10 true
Cuboid crazy: 2
1 true 2 false 3 true 4 true
5 true 6 true 7 true 8 true
9 true 10 true 11 true 12 false

Cut it out! – page 64
There may be more than one solution for some of the shapes.

House building – page 65
H, D, G, F, B, E, C, A

Logical thinking – page 66
1 pink green green green
red yellow red blue

2 red yellow red blue   or   red yellow red blue
green green pink red   green green pink green
red
3 pink green green   green green green pink
green green yellow   or   green red green
4 red yellow blue orange
white purple green pink

Equation persuasion – page 67
The equations are all true for this set of numbers.
Now try this!
It is not possible to use different numbers that make ALL the statements true, but it is possible to make some of them true.

Animal magic – page 68
1 a 1 b 4   2 a 5 b 3   3 a 5 b 2
4 a 5 b 7   5 a 6 b 4   6 a 7 b 3

Grid riddles – page 69
1 11   2 12   3 45   4 10   5 60   6 2
  13   8   32   18   33   250   3
7 B − A = C   8 (A ×2) + B = C   9 (A − B) ÷ 2
  75   225   7

Conveyor belts – page 72
Prime 53 59 61 67 71 73 79 83 89 97
Not prime – all even numbers and the following odd numbers: 51, 55, 57, 63, 65, 69, 75, 77, 81, 85, 87, 91, 93, 95, 99

Prime suspect – page 73
The dots joined in order should show a castle.
Now try this!
There are many examples, such as:
2 + 7 = 9   13 + 3 = 16   23 + 2 = 25   31 + 5 = 36   47 + 2 = 49 etc.

Sponsored sports – page 74
1 £2.15 2 Yes 3 27 4 £4.81
5 £9.75 6 £2.34 7 (a) £15.64 (b) £22.18
Now try this!
£41.23, or £66.48 if they include Leon and Emma's sponsorship money.

Shape sort: 2 – page 76

3-D detective – page 77
1 d 2 c 3 f 4 b 5 e 6 a

Tetrahedra – page 78
Now try this!
The shape is a dodecahedron.
It has 12 faces, 8 vertices and 18 edges.

Table challenges – page 79

	Number of cakes				
Number of teas	0	1	2	3	4
0		60p	£1.20	£1.80	£2.40
1	£1.20	£1.80	£2.40	£3	£3.60
2	£2.40	£3	£3.60	£4.20	£4.80
3	£3.60	£4.20	£4.80	£5.40	£6
4	£4.80	£5.40	£6	£6.60	£7.20

	Number of cans of cola				
Number of magazines	0	1	2	3	4
0		55p	£1.10	£1.65	£2.20
1	75p	£1.30	£1.85	£2.40	£2.95
2	£1.50	£2.05	£2.60	£3.15	£3.70
3	£2.25	£2.80	£3.35	£3.90	£4.45
4	£3	£3.55	£4.10	£4.65	£5.20

Square numbers – page 80
1 This is always true.   2 This is always true.
3 This is always true.   4 This is always true.
5 This is sometimes true.   6 This is always true.

A general rule – page 81
Now try this!
1 Number of days = 7n
2 Number of months = 12n
3 Number of weeks = 52n
4 Cost in pounds = 11n
5 Cost in pounds = 50 − 6n
Maximum value for n = 8

Formula fun – page 82
1 60 + n   2 x − 3
3 2b or 2 × b   4 ½p or p ÷ 2
5 a + b   6 5x − x or 4x
7 y + 6   8 x − y
9 19 + 7 − x or 16 − x   10 12 − y

Square secrets – page 83
quadrat vierkant cuadrado firkant

Magic squares – page 84

×0.3 (4.5):
1.2	0.9	2.4
2.7	1.5	0.3
0.6	2.1	1.8

×0.4 (6):
1.6	1.2	3.2
3.6	2	0.4
0.8	2.8	2.4

×0.6 (9):
2.4	1.8	4.8
5.4	3	0.6
1.2	4.2	3.6

×0.7 (10.5):
2.8	2.1	5.6
6.3	3.5	0.7
1.4	4.9	4.2

×0.8 (12):
3.2	2.4	6.4
7.2	4	0.8
1.6	5.6	4.8

×0.9 (13.5):
3.6	2.7	7.2
8.1	4.5	0.9
1.8	6.3	5.4

Now try this!
9.8	9.4	11.4
11.8	10.2	8.6
9	11	10.6
30.6, yes

Prime factor compactor – page 85
Now try this!
Yes, all numbers (other than primes themselves) can be written as a product of prime factors.

American football – page 86
1 18   2 30   3 45   4 44   5 24   6 140
7 56   8 210   9 440
Now try this!
(a) 2 × 2 × 3   (b) 2 × 2 × 2 × 5   (c) 2 × 5 × 5
(d) 2 × 2 × 2 × 7   (e) 2 × 7 × 7   (f) 5 × 5 × 5
(g) 2 × 2 × 2 × 2 × 2

3 1000kg 4 360kg 5 150kg
6 £25.50 7 450kg 8 £59.70

Nutritional numbers – page 143
1 0.4g 0.4g 0.21g   2 3.6g 11.2g 1.8g
3 1.8g 31.5g 17.5g   4 13g 87.3g 52.8g
5 3.6g 14.4g 99.9g   6 110kcal 237kcal 1008kcal

Revolution solutions – page 144
1 120°   2 120°   3 120°   4 240°   5 45°   6 150°
7 135°

Angle tangle – page 146
a 68°   b 14°   c 89°   d 47°   e 110°   f 114°
g 64°   h 117°   i 132°   j 48°   k 75°   l 12°
m 136°

They do, duvet? – page 147
a 17°   b 71°   c 37°   d 11°   e 25°   f 88°
g 56°   h 54°   i 54°   j 110°   k 35°

Get to the point – page 148
105°, 40°, 231°, 54°, 92°, 157°, 128°, 136°, 24°, 63°,
163°, 23°, 51°, 188°, 90°
COLOUR ALL THE REFLEX ANGLES
YELLOW

Coded coordinates – page 149
There may be more than one solution for some
questions:
(a) AFHB   (b) HDGI   (c) BCFE
(d) ACB   (e) EFIH

Reflection selection – page 151
1 (5, 5) (8, 5) (8, 3) (6, 3)
  (5, 5) (5, 8) (3, 8) (3, 6)
2 (2, 3) (1, 5) (2, 6) (3, 4)   3 (6, 4) (8, 2) (6, 0) (4, 2)
3 (2, 3) (5, 1) (6, 2) (4, 3)   (4, 2) (2, 8) (0, 6) (2, 4)
4 (3, 6) (1, 7) (7, 7) (5, 6)   5 (3, 4) (1, 7) (5, 7)
  (6, 3) (7, 1) (7, 7) (6, 5)   (4, 3) (7, 1) (7, 5)

Dimitri's day – page 154
1 a 1 hr 35 mins
  b 1 hr 55 mins
  c 50 mins   2 18 mins
3 22 mins   4 14 mins   5 28 mins
6 22 mins   8 16:30

Scale drawings – page 155
The new drawings should have the following
dimensions.
1 1.4cm × 1.6cm   2 1.2cm × 1.1 cm
3 2.9cm × 1.7cm   4 1.2cm × 1.5cm
5 1.6 cm × 0.8 cm

Gemstone necklace – page 156
1 7.5 and 2.7   2 8.5 and 5.3
  8.1   1.5   21.2   1.7
3 9.4 and 6.3   4 9.2 and 7.6
  31.5   4.7   45.6   2.3

Time after time – page 158
1 12   2 5 hrs 50 mins
3 28 mins   4 7 mins
5 2 hrs 32 mins 6 9
7 20 hrs 25 mins 8 3 hrs 25 mins
9 9 mins 50 secs

Quick conversions – page 159
52 mm   7090 m   0.16 m   2.04 km
8.7 cm   7340 m   0.35 kg   412 cm
10 ml   38 mm   6720 m   90 cm
620 000 ml 3200 cm   0.05 km   548.2 cm

Now try this!
Martina (As the mean time is actually more than
9.92 seconds, it is nearer to 9.93 seconds than to
9.91 seconds)

Shady business – page 128
A There should be more sections shaded black
  than criss-cross.
B There should be more sections dotted than left
  white.
C All sections should be dotted.
D There should be the same number of sections
  coloured green as red.
E There should be no sections coloured red.
F There should be at least three sections
  coloured green.
G There should be two sections coloured green or
  blue.
H There should be no sections coloured green or
  left white.

Arrow error – page 132
1 Correct   2 Incorrect   3 Correct
4 Correct   5 Incorrect   6 Correct
7 Correct   8 Correct   9 Incorrect

Patrick's patterns – page 133
1 15cm × 15cm   2 14cm × 17cm
3 15cm × 18cm   4 19cm × 13cm
5 11cm × 14cm   6 9cm × 12cm

Model thinking – page 134
1 9cm   2 11cm   3 9cm   4 16cm
5 8cm   6 12cm   7 10cm   8 16cm

Dragon trail – page 135
If correctly completed the trail of remainders
should go from the top right-hand side around
and down to the bottom.
Now try this!
53, 56, 59, 62, ... 95, 98

Shopping parade – page 136
1 22.89m   2 5.12m   3 £11.13
4 11.25kg   5 £47.16   6 £26.32
7 £11.12   8 £10.68   9 £26.04

Best estimate – page 137
1 25m   2 1g   3 2litres   4 600cm²   5 300mm
6 4m²   7 80cm   8 30g   9 350km

Measure up: 1 – page 138
1 24ml + 38ml + 12ml = 74ml
2 18ml + 12ml + 48ml = 78ml
3 21ml + 27ml + 7ml = 55ml
4 18ml + 36ml + 42ml = 96ml

Measure up: 2 – page 139
1 a 400g   B = 460g   C = 750g   D = 800g
  E = 450g   F = 280g   G = 650g   H = 700g
D, C, H, G, B, E, A, F

Perimeter patterns – page 140
1 34cm   2 36cm   3 50cm
4 48cm   5 50cm   6 66cm
7 36cm   8 56cm   9 80cm

Rectangular reasoning – page 141
Perimeter
1 66cm   2 58cm   3 48cm
4 38cm   5 66cm   6 84cm
Area
1 203cm²   2 168cm²   3 88cm²
4 45cm²   5 208cm²   6 404cm²

Rocky's wall and rockery – page 142
1 720m   2 a $\frac{1}{3}$ b $\frac{1}{4}$ $\frac{5}{12}$

In the science lab – page 119
A = 400g B = 460g C = 750g D = 800g
E = 450g F = 280g G = 650g H = 700g
D, C, H, G, B, E, A, F

In conclusion: 1 – page 120
1 3   2 17
3 The results show that this girls' team
  performed better than this boys' team. To
  be able to say in general whether girls are
  better than boys at football, you need more
  information.

In conclusion: 2 – page 121
1 Classes 2, 5 and 6   2 £72
3 The pie chart shows that Class 4 raised the
  most money. This might be because it is best
  at sport, but it might be because more people
  sponsored the children or people paid more
  money each time.
4 Again, the pie chart shows that Class 4 raised
  the most money. This might be because it
  cares most about charity, but it might be
  because more people sponsored the children
  or people paid more money each time, or
  Class 4 are better at sport.

In conclusion: 3 – page 122
1 July and August   2 3°C
3 March   4 80mm
5 The graphs only show the results for one year.
  You would need to look at the results from
  many more years to say whether London or
  Rome has more rain each year.
6 The graphs do seem to show this but you
  would need the results for other years to be
  able to say whether this is true or not.

Miles to kilometres – page 124
(Accept answers +1 those given.)
1 a 80km   b 160km   c 16km
  d 100km   e 56km
2 a 25miles   b 75miles   c 59miles
  d 3 miles   e 93miles
3 a 1.6 km   b 0.6 miles
Now try this!
Divide each by 50

Per 100 grams – page 125
1 5g
2 10g
3

Mass of bar	Protein	Carbohydrate	Fat	Fibre
200g	20g	160g	10g	10g
50g	5g	40g	2.5g	2.5g
120g	12g	96g	6g	6g
175g	17.5g	140g	8.75g	8.75g

Cheeky Chalky – page 126
1 a 11 b a number ≥ 31 c 85.6 d 17 e 7, 7
  f one number ≤ £16 and one number ≥ 16
  g any two numbers which total 5
2 a c   3 a c
6.2, 3.7, 9.1 and 16, 10, 8 should be ringed.

Beijing 2008 – page 127
1 a Bolt   b Thompson   c Dix
2 0.20 seconds   3 9.92 seconds
4 0.23 seconds   5 9.94 seconds (middle two
  times added and divided by 2)
6 a 30 years 8 months   b 21 years 11 months
7 8 years 9 months

Primes, squares and multiples – page 87
Some have several possible answers. Example
answers are:

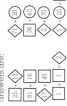

Cutting corners – page 89
1 500g box 2 9-pack 3 4-pack
4 340g box 5 54g tin

Dodecahedra – page 91
Three edges meet at each vertex. Each face is
joined to five others.

Finding out – page 96
The answers for this activity will depend upon
the children's ideas. The easiest investigation
is that in question C, because it uses data that is
already known.

Testing times – page 97
1 4   2 8   3 31   4 no
Now try this!
£1205.

You are what you eat – page 98
1 a 5   2 a fruit b margarine
3 a 40g b 60g c 120g d 50g e 90g
4 a $\frac{5}{12}$ b $\frac{3}{12}$ or $\frac{1}{4}$ c $\frac{1}{12}$ d $\frac{2}{12}$ or $\frac{1}{6}$ e $\frac{1}{12}$
5 a 10 b 6 c 2 d 4 e 2

Home on the range: 1 and 2 – page 99
3 The range shows whether the data is all
  similar in size or whether it is spread out.

Different modes: 1 – page 101
cat   yellow   car

Different modes: 2 – page 102
banana   sparrow   5

Paul's pool party – page 103
1 13   2 10   3 26°C   4 11   5 16

In the middle: 1 – page 104
4.5 should be ringed. 10y 4m should be ringed.
Now try this!
Check that the fourth number is 43.

In the middle: 2 – page 105
1 should be ringed. 11 should be ringed.

Weather station – page 106
The answers will be based on the children's
ideas, which can be linked to science and
geography. Check that the children's ideas will
lead to data being collected and represented
fairly.

Salad bar – page 107
Frequencies for the week:
Grated carrot 57   Sweetcorn 26   Lettuce 48
Beetroot 49   Mixed pepper 66   Cucumber 52

---

1 mixed pepper
2 49   3 sweetcorn 4 Tuesday
5 a sweetcorn b Thursday
6 caterers/suppliers
Now try this!
The statement is true. 60 portions of salad were
served on Friday.

Stretchy statistics: 1 and 2 – page 108
1 8.3cm   2 12.5cm   3 9.75cm
Now try this!
B

Plant scale: 1 – page 110
1 a 16 b 4   2 32   3 49   4 9   5 week 3
6 weeks 1, 3 and 4   7 week 1   8 41
Now try this!
Cacti, because proportionally fewer of these are
sold and in week 2, no cacti were sold.

Side orders – page 112

	Range	Mean	Median	Mode
Onion rings	11	5.3	4	3
Garlic bread	6	5.4	5	5, 7
Chips	10	12.9	12	12
Green salad	10	7.9	7	7
Mixed peppers	13	10.4	11	11

Best average – page 113
1 mean 45, median 44, mode 38. The mean, as it
  is between all the scores.
2 mean 3, median 2, mode 1. The median, as
  it shows that half the people own few or no
  pets.
3 mean 4.2, median 4, mode 5. The median, as
  most people asked have a shoe size that is
  about this size – only one has size 2 and one
  size 6.
Now try this!
The score that Sophie would be most likely
to choose is the mean, as this has the highest
value.

Chess guess: 1 and 2 – page 115
1 a knight or a queen
  b a rook or a white piece
  c a pawn or a black piece
  d a black piece or a bishop
  e a knight or a rook
  f a white king or a black rook
2 a pawn
  b Because there are more pawns on the board
  than any other type of chess piece.
3 a queen
Now try this!
The girl is right. There is the same number of
kings as queens so Sam is equally likely to pick
a king as a queen.

Chance landing – page 117
1 A   2 A
3 a false   b false   c false
4 a fifty-fifty chance   c false
  b false   d fifty-fifty chance
  c unlikely
Now try this!
Neither, they are both equally likely.

Can you do better? – page 118
Different answers could be justified.
1 25cm 2 2m 3 50ml 4 6001 5 1500kg
6 367km 7 3460km 8 180g 9 3m 10 10g
11 1m 12 40000km 13 8.51 14 99.5m
15 3cm

7.6 kg   1.08 m   8 cm   4050 ml
0.7 m   49 700 mm

Full scale ahead – page 160
1 100 ml   2 30 kg   3 30 ml   4 1000 g
5 3500 g   6 100 km   7 20 kg   8 0.3 m
Now try this!
4.5 kg

Rubber sizes – page 161
1 2.9 cm, 2.9 cm   2 3.6 cm, 2.8 cm
3 5.2 cm   4 3.8 cm, 2.6 cm
5 5.1 cm   6 3.6 cm, 2.3 cm
7 2.1 cm, 2.4 cm   8 4.6 cm, 1.5 cm

Half squares – page 162
a 3 cm²   b 3 cm²   c 2 cm²   d 6½ cm²
e 4½ cm² f 3 cm²   g 1½ cm² h 5½ cm²
i 2½ cm² j 4½ cm² k 4 cm²   l 5 cm²

Something fishy – page 163
A 16 cm²   B 14.5 cm²   C 12 cm²
D 10.5 cm² E 13 cm²   F 13.5 cm²
G 14 cm²   H 15.5 cm²   I 21.5 cm²
J 16.5 cm² K 27 cm²   L 16.5 cm²

Carpet calculations – page 164
Hall 24.75 m²   Lounge 72.2 m²
Office 39.96 m² Kitchen 58.09 m²
Now try this!
£301.95 + £718.39 + £337.66 + £667.45 = £2025.45

Fun at the fair – page 165
1 5 × 5p, 5 × 20p
2 6 × 10p, 6 × 20p or 9 × 10p, 9 × 10p or 3 × 50p, 3 × 10p
3 11 × 2p, 11 × £1 4 9 × £1 5 7 × 2p, 7 × 50p 6 9 × 5p, 9 × 20p

Dancing dilemma – page 166
Mrs Pandit, Miss Lee, Mr Taki, Mr Fox, Miss Jones and Mr Simpson.
Now try this!
Mrs Pandit and Mr Simpson, Miss Lee and Mr Taki, Miss Jones and Mr Fox.

Talking points: 1 – page 167
1 Yes, if the original number is even.
2 Yes, if the original number is a multiple of 5 (or ends in a 0 or 5).
3 Yes, if the original number is even.
4 Yes, if the original number is even.
5 Yes, if the original number ends in a 1 or 6.
6 Yes, if the original number is a multiple of 6.
7 Yes, if the original number is a multiple of 6.
8 Yes, if the original number ends in .25 or .75 (or ¼, ¾).
9 Yes, if the original number is even.
10 Yes, if the original number is a multiple of 8.

Talking points: 2 – page 168
1 Yes, if the original number is odd.
2 Yes, if the original number ends in a 2 or 7.
3 Yes, if the original number ends in .5 (or ½).
4 Yes, if the original number is odd.
5 Yes, if the original number is even.
6 Yes, if the original number ends in a 2 or 7.
7 Yes, if the original number ends in a 1.
8 Yes, if the original number ends in a 2 or 7.
9 Yes, if the original number ends in .5 (or ½).
10 Yes, if the original number is a multiple of 4.

Farming fractions – page 169
Field A 6 horses, 20 cows, 25 sheep (60 animals)
Field B 10 horses, 20 cows, 25 sheep (60 animals)
Field C 30 horses, 21 cows, 35 sheep (105 animals)

Copy cats – page 170
1 180 mm × 120 mm   2 120 mm × 180 mm
3 60 mm × 90 mm   4 66 mm × 99 mm

Planet exploration – page 171

	Earth	Mercury	Venus	Uranus	Mars
James	37kg	11.1kg	333kg	246kg	14.8kg
Chloe	46kg	13.8kg	414.4kg	36.8kg	18.4kg

Pack it in – page 172
Now try this!

How are we related? – page 173

Fraction quiz – page 174

A sure measure – page 175
Now try this!

Sorting session – page 176
Now try this!

Fraction satisfaction – page 177
Now try this!
7/10 of 840 = 588

Hens and chicks – page 178
Now try this!

Puzzle patterns – page 181
1 Alfie pours 12 and Billy pours 8.
2 8 × 10 cm and 7 × 6 cm
3 10 × 500 g and 20 × 300 g
4 15 × £5 and 25 × £3

How did you work it out? – page 182
1 352 (or 353 if a leap year)   2 14 × 15
3 Either a pentagon (with two right angles and
three angles of 120°) or a trapezium (with two
angles of 120° and two angles of 60°).

Extreme sports – page 184
1 (a) £112 500   (b) £22 500
3 £7500
4 (a) £108 750   (b) £13 750   (c) £1250
5 (a) £178 750   (b) £57 750   (c) £16 500
   (d) £11 000   (e) £8250   (f) £22750

Robot twins – page 186

I scream for ice-cream – page 187

Percentage code – page 188
Two out of five

gBay – page 189
84%, 80%, 84%, 95%, 86%, 80%, 75%, 90%, 96%,
90%, 84%, 87%, 30%, 90%, 90%, 91%

Book boxes – page 191
Now try this!
1104 boxes

Quotient quiz – page 192
1 17.4   2 22.25   3 7.6   4 24.75   5 10.5
6 12.25   7 15.5   8 19.8   9 18.5   10 10.75
Alice won the quiz.

Fraction-packed shapes – page 193
The new shapes should be as follows:
1 square with sides 60mm
2 rectangle with perimeter 216 mm (e.g. 48 mm × 60 mm)
3 rectangle with perimeter 208 mm (e.g. 64 mm × 40 mm)
4 rectangle with perimeter 150 mm (e.g. 51 mm × 24 mm)
5 rectangle with sides 104 mm × 33mm
Now try this!
The diameters of the circles should be: 20 cm,
16 cm, 12cm

Great grams – page 195
1 a £1.80   b £1.60
e 90p   f £2
2 a 400 g   b 300 g   c 200 g   d 300 g
   e 250 g   f 250 g   g 225 g   h 1000 g
   i 125 g   j 175 g   k 325 g   l 450 g

A matter of balance: 1 – page 196
1 m + 3 kg = 8 kg, m = 5 kg
2 m + 4 kg = 7 kg, m = 3 kg
3 m + 2 kg = 7 kg, m = 5 kg
4 m + 5 kg = 7 kg, m = 2 kg
5 m + 3 kg = 8 kg, m = 5 kg
6 m + 3 kg = 10 kg, m = 7 kg
7 m + 4 kg = 5 kg, m = 1 kg
8 m + 4 kg = 10 kg, m = 6 kg
9 m + 2 kg = 9 kg, m = 7 kg

A matter of balance: 2 – page 197
1 2m + 3 kg = 5 kg, m = 1 kg
2 2m + 2 kg = 5 kg, m = 1.5 kg
3 2m + 1 kg = 7 kg, m = 3 kg
4 3m + 1 kg = 4 kg, m = 1 kg
5 3m + 1 kg = 4 kg, m = 1 kg
6 4m + 1 kg = 3 kg, m = 0.5 kg
7 4m + 4 kg = 5 kg, m = 0.25 kg
8 2m + 2 kg = 9 kg, m = 3.5 kg
9 4m + 2 kg = 7 kg, m = 1.25 kg

Gas bill changes – page 198
1 £297   2 £792   3 £118.80
Now try this!
The answers are the same, as an increase of
10% (equivalent to × 1.1) and a reduction of
10% (equivalent to × 0.9) can be done in any order.

'Expert' deals – page 199
Any order produces the same discount.
Now try this!
Best price: TV £273.60   Laptop £342
            Hi-fi £410.40   DVD player £205.20
Saving: TV £126.40   Laptop £158
           Hi-fi £189.60   DVD player £94.80

Courgette croquettes – page 200
1000 g courgettes   250 g onions
125 g feta cheese   500 g potatoes
200 g breadcrumbs   120 g flour
Total mass = 2195 g
Now try this!
1400 g courgettes   350 g onions
175 g feta cheese
700 g potatoes   280 g breadcrumbs
168 g flour

Precision division – page 202
1 79   2 52   3 64   4 53   5 92
6 27   7 59   8 65   9 64   10 72
Now try this!
(a) 79   (b) 66   (c) 34   (d) 49   (e) 58   (f) 78

Division patterns – page 203
0.6   60
1.9   190
2.8   280
5.7   570
5.7   570
5.7   570
12.7   127   1270
15.3   153   1530
7.7   77   770
Now try this!
0.57   0.77   1.27

Soiled goods – page 204
1 £9.54   2 £26.65   3 £14.08   4 76p
5 £4.16   6 £25.18   7 67p   8 40p
8 £19.84
Now try this!
£143.30

Fraction spell – page 206
CHOMP   CRAWL   SHINY   BLACK   BEAST

Telly addict – page 207
45 mins, 30 mins, 9 mins, 42 mins, 44 mins,
20 mins, 26 mins,
3 mins, 10 mins, 15 mins, 24 mins, 18 mins,
40 mins
Now try this!

Hoopla stall – page 208
40%   60%   75%   15%   90%
25%   35%   64%

Colour it! – page 209
1 3 shapes blue
2 4 shapes yellow and 1 red
3 7 shapes green and 2 blue
4 6 shapes yellow, 3 red and 4 green
5 3 shapes green and 1 red
6 9 shapes blue, 1 red and 7 yellow
7 2 shapes blue, 6 red and 10 yellow
8 11 shapes red, 24 yellow and 1 blue
9 1 shape green, 4 yellow and 7 red
Now try this!
1 25%   2 50%   3 10%   4 35%   5 20%
6 15%   7 25%   8 28%   9 52%

Team work – page 210
There may be more than one appropriate
answer for each situation but the most
appropriate for each is shown here.
1 4 r2   2 4.5   4 5   5 4.5
6 4   7 5   8 £4.05   9 4 r2   10 4½

Are we nearly there? – page 212
1 40 km   2 43 km   3 48 km   4 50 km   5 54 km
Now try this!
a 120 km, 135 km, 144 km, 150 km, 162 km
b 60 km, 67.5 km, 72 km, 75 km, 81 km

Cooking crisis – page 213
1 225 g   3 420 g
270 g   960 g   490 g
450 ml 160 g   140 g
126 ml 16   245 g
9   1120 g   7
        720 g   259 g
Now try this!
1 250 g   2 10   3 600 g
300 g   700 g
500 g   1200 g   200 g
140 g   200 ml   350 g
10   20   10
         1400 g   370 g
         900 g

216